...AND NO PURPLE HEART

by
Frank Reese Mays

Briarwood Publications, Incorporated

Copyright © 1999 Briarwood Publications Inc.

First Published 1999
Briarwood Publications & Sassy Cat Books, Inc.
150 West College Street
Rocky Mount, Virginia 24151

Frank Reese Mays

AND NO PURPLE HEART
ISBN 1-892614-16-2

Manufactured in the United States of America.

Printed by Briarwood Publications, Inc.

Frank Reese Mays
1944
age 19

"We have nothing to fear, but fear itself."
Franklin D. Roosevelt, 1941

...and No Purple Heart

This is a story based on actual events in the life of the author during his time of service in World War II. The combat missions, dates, blood, tears, and events are all too real.

There was no fear for the author, death became a thing to expect. *Just let death be quick, his friends would welcome him.* It was an honor to serve his country and fellow man. The American flag, or a military band can still bring a tear and a chill over him.

He once read, "A friend is not one who is taken in by sham, but one who knows your faults and doesn't give a damn." Frank Reese Mays had friends like that. He lost them all, before he was 21 years old, while he was learning to be a man.

On his chest, he proudly wore his combat badges:

> The Distinguished Flying Cross
> The Air Medal with four Oak Leaf Clusters
> The European Battle Ribbon with a Silver Star
> The Good Conduct Medal
> A Presidential Citation
> His Silver Wings over a blue Combat Patch . . .
>
> *AND NO PURPLE HEART*!

OPERATION OVERLORD
June 6, 1944

D-DAY REMEMBERED

Listen, a sound of voice in prayer
a hush falls over the restless stir
among the rows of white markers

Still the sun does not set.

The young, the aged, all come to remember
with speeches and tears,
the distant wail of TAPS,

Still, the sun does not set

Ceremonies completed,
accolades echo over the greens
across the beaches, out to the channel beyond,

Still the sun does not set

Shells bursting, guns firing,
anguish cries, it all now returns,
'twas a moment in eternity,

Still the sun does not set

All who were there that day,
they that were so close, the families, a nation,
until the last of all draws a final breath

The sun will not set on this day.

Frank Reese Mays
June 6, 1998

I want to dedicate this book to the other nine men of the crew who served with me aboard the War Horse and to my wife and children who have put up with me since.

The events and characters in this story are true. With the exception of notable historical figures, the names have been changed by the author.

CHAPTER 1

The D-Day Invasion

Sitting in the ball turret hanging beneath the fuselage of the B-17 Flying Fortress, Frank Mays could do little but watch. Except for the intercom system of the airplane, he was cut off from human connection—*alone*. The snug space in the turret was a lonesome place and at times, it felt like he was *SITTING ON THE DOORSTEP OF HELL.*

As Frank watched through the 18-inch round glass between his feet, anti-aircraft shells bursting all around him, it seemed as if he were in a black cloud. Flak or shrapnel from the bursting shells filled the air with thousands of steel fragments, as flashes of fire from burst after burst lit the awakening morning sky. Frank could do little but imagine himself as small as possible throughout the hellish barrage. All ten men aboard the airplane were quiet as the formation continued the bombing run. The bombardier was preparing the Norden bombsight, fixing the crosshairs on the target below, as shells burst ever closer to the airplane.

Frank scanned the underbelly of the plane looking for damage caused by the strewn shrapnel. The superchargers on each engine spewed a blue-white exhaust flame, indicating that the four 1200-horsepower radial engines were running smoothly. Still, the B-17 bounced and jerked from the concussions of the bursting shells, requiring the pilot and co-pilot to struggle to keep the plane in level flight in the formation of B-17s. Frank was jarred from side to side in his turret as he kept the turret moving to help deflect flying shards of shrapnel.

Suddenly a shell burst directly in front of the turret sight glass, sending shrapnel into the metal body of the airplane, and damaging the number 3 engine. The co-pilot quickly feathered the propeller and shut down the engine as black fluid streamed underneath the wing from a ruptured oil line. Fortunately, Frank could see only minor damage to the underside of the wing near where the flak had hit.

Red flashes and black smoke from bursting shells seemed closer now as the formation reached the IP, or the Initial Point of the bomb run. It seemed that the German anti-aircraft gunners now had the correct altitude of the formation and shells were bursting closer and more frequently around the planes.

The pilot turned control over to the bombardier, and the bombsight took control of flying the plane by its connection through the automatic pilot. Frank watched the bomb bay doors open and counted the thirty-eight 100-pound bombs as they dropped.

Frank could see the bombs exploding some 17,000 feet below, in the water, just off the Channel shoreline of France. The target was a concrete and steel barrier placed there to prevent military landing craft from coming ashore. There were explosions along the beach as naval guns on Allied ships bombarded the gun positions of the defending Germans. Frank looked at his wristwatch and noted the time: 6:15 a.m.

Hundreds of Allied ships and smaller boats cluttered the Channel and the warships kept a constant barrage of shells pounding the German gun positions. Troop transport ships sat at anchor unloading thousands of American soldiers in smaller troop landing-craft, creating a beehive of activity on the waters below the bomber formation.

Frank rotated his turret up and looked toward England. In the early morning haze, he saw a stream of American bombers leaving England and following his airplane. Stretching as far as his eyes could see were hundreds of B-17 and B-24 heavy bombers, flying in a continuous formation, without a gap. As he rotated the turret forward, a shell burst nearby and a piece of flak cut through a small Plexiglas window at Frank's side. The piece of hot shrapnel struck a metal gun casing on one of the .50-caliber machine guns and then ricocheted into Frank's left fur-lined boot. Fortunately, the thick material of the boot stopped the piece of flak just short of cutting his skin. Although it hurt like crazy, Frank could tell he was not bleeding as he saw the piece of shrapnel sticking from his boot just forward of his heel near the instep. With no blood flowing, there would, of course, be no Purple Heart.

"Those bastards are trying to kill me!" he muttered, as cold wind whistled through the broken window. The fur-lined flight suits were not designed to protect against winds of 170 miles per hour at 45 degrees below zero, so Frank turned the turret to position the broken window toward the rear of the plane. This helped some, but only temporarily, as he had to keep the turret moving to watch for German attack fighters. So far, none had been reported in the area, but they were expected to appear at any time. The flak continued to chew up the formation, with other planes taking hits, although none were close to Frank's plane at this time.

As quickly as the flak started, it suddenly stopped. Frank imagined the Germans must have been having a hard time trying to decide which targets to select. He could see many low-flying Allied bombers and fighter planes attacking below and to the sides of the heavy bomber targets, as bombs and naval shelling pulverized the entire coastal area. As he looked forward, he noticed the bomber formations ahead were now starting to make a turn to the right. The 385th Heavy Bomb Group was near the lead in the air armada consisting of hundreds and hundreds of heavy bombers.

The French countryside appeared below as a patchwork of small fields surrounded by hedgerows. Frank noticed that the roofs of most of the scattered houses he could see were the color of red clay tile. Here, away from the beaches, the setting looked peaceful. From three miles up, he could not distinguish anything smaller than a military truck, but he knew that many soldiers were on the move down there. The flak had long stopped and now the drone of the airplane engines lulled a false sense of security. Fortunately, no one in his airplane had been injured, and the expected German fighters had not appeared. Frank kept the turret turned such that the wind no longer whistled through the broken window at his side, and his mind began to wander back to the pre-flight briefing earlier in the morning.

The briefing officer had stated, "Okay boys, this is it—the day the world has been waiting for. Today we start the invasion of the Continent and give the Germans hell. Allied troops will disembark from England and hit the beaches along the French coast."

The Major called it "Operation Overlord." Disembarkation Day—*D-DAY,* Tuesday, June 6, 1944.

Paratroopers were being dropped in France at the time of the briefing, and they now fought a short distance inland from the Channel. Their job was to interrupt German movement toward the Channel. The invasion by American troops would be on the beach of Normandy, France, near a city called Caen.

The crew loading-list for this mission had been posted at 10:30 p.m. the previous night, and Frank was roused from the sack at 1:30 this morning. It had been a typical British morning with cool, dark and damp clouds thickening over the area. The clouds had now begun to move over the Channel. They were slow moving, watery clouds—not a good sign for the troops below.

As the formation of 35 airplanes flew from France over the English Channel and headed back to base at Great Ashfield in Suffolk, England, the gathering clouds to the west darkened.

Once on the ground back at the base, the ground crews began repairing the ruptured oil line and broken window. When the fuel tanker arrived, the B-17 was fueled, and then more bombs were loaded. An hour after the wheels touched down from the first mission, the repairs were completed and Frank's plane rolled off the concrete hardstand onto the taxi strip to commence their second mission of the day.

Frank's crew had arrived at the 385th Bomb Group on June 1 and had flown their first mission on Sunday,

June 4, bombing a target near Versailles, France. On their second mission on June 5, they had bombed some beach guns at Caen. The count was now Mission number 3, D-Day June 6th minus 1, and today's second mission would be number four. They were heading back to the invasion beachhead at Normandy.

As the 35 airplanes from the 385th rejoined the air armada, it was a remarkable sight with all the many Allied bombers filling the sky, creating a never-ending line of aircraft heading toward France. Through the gathering clouds, Frank could see the wakes of the ships below, along with flashes of fire and billows of black smoke from the shipboard guns. The shoreline was being pulverized by a combination of naval shells and bombs dropped from the air. From where the shells were bursting on the shore, Frank could tell that the ground troops were not making much headway onto the beaches. It had to be pure hell down there with the Germans holding their positions in the face of all the firepower. He had learned in briefings that the Germans were well fortified along the shore with many heavy, concrete gun emplacements.

As the formation of airplanes in which Frank was flying crossed the Normandy coastline, he again saw Caen off to his left at about 9 o'clock. The German fighters that had been absent on the first mission now suddenly appeared from the high clouds. He heard someone yell over the intercom that there were ten ME-109s coming in at 10 o'clock high. The plane began to vibrate from the firing of .50-caliber machine guns in the top turret and waist gunner's positions.

A B-17 from an upper element of the formation fell away at 4 o'clock, going down with its numbers 2 and 3 engines on fire. The bomber started to roll over on its side and as it did, the plane exploded.

Another B-17 drifted down and underneath Frank, with the number 3 engine on fire. He watched as a man bailed out of the fuselage waist door, his parachute blooming full open. Then a second man jumped and his parachute opened too soon, snagging the horizontal tail elevator, causing the man to be strung out behind the plane like a tail on a kite. The fire in the number 3 engine immediately flared back to the parachute and melted it into nothingness. Frank watched as the man then fell end-over-end without his parachute and disappeared into the background of the earth. "God, what a horrible way to die," thought Frank.

No other chutes appeared from the airplane before it rolled upside down and exploded. The thirty-eight 100-pound bombs and gasoline tore the plane into small pieces and debris drifted toward the ground. At that moment, all the other planes in the formation dropped their bombs.

The German fighters came back and Frank fired at a ME-109 as it flew under his plane—but *no cigar*, as he missed the fighter. The flak started again and suddenly the fighters were gone. The formation then turned and as they crossed the coast heading for home, Frank saw Cherbourg off at 9 o'clock. There were explosions around the edges of the town.

Over England, the pilot announced that the crew could come off oxygen, so Frank stored the ball turret and removed his oxygen mask. Alex and King sat in the fuselage waist with him and lit cigarettes. No one mentioned seeing the man falling without his chute nor was there any comment concerning the B-17 blowing up. No one ever discussed these type incidents; instead, they just sat and thought about the carnage they had seen.

There were more than a dozen other bomber bases around Great Ashfield, located three to five miles apart. From the air, they all looked similar. Great Ashfield was easy to spot from the air because of the three tall poplar trees that threw shadows when the 385th returned from a mission.

The formation went into a circular landing pattern and with only one engine out and no one injured, Frank's plane was one of the last to land. King and Frank were looking out the right waist gunner's window as the wheels touched the landing strip. When the right wheel touched down, the tire blew, sending the plane off the runway and across the grass at more than 100 miles an hour. At the sound of the tire blowing, the pilot shut down the three remaining engines and tried to hold the plane in a straight path as it raced across the grassy area between runways.

The plane had traveled only about 200 feet when the right landing gear dropped into a drainage hole and spun the airplane around, digging one wing into the ground. The sudden stop tore loose Frank's grip on the window frame and threw him forward onto his back, with King and Alex landing atop him. They were a mess of arms and legs as they piled on top of each other. Frank's back hit across a metal floor frame knocking the wind from him. Although the fall hurt his back and neck, he and the two gunners quickly scrambled from the airplane and ran about 100 feet before they realized the airplane was not on fire. The other gunners and officers were not far behind.

The B-17 was not a pretty sight lying there with one

wing stuck in the ground and the other high in the air. Both propellers on the right wing were badly damaged and gas poured from the ruptured wing tanks. This, of course, ended their flying for the day. The wheels had left the runway at 3:00 a.m. for the first mission and it was now after 3:00 p.m. Frank thought that two combat missions and a crash landing were enough for one day. Everyone on the crew was tired and ready for a meal and a shot of Scotch whiskey at the mess hall.

The clouds had rolled in and a sprinkle of rain began to fall as the men gathered equipment from the plane, returned the flight equipment to supply and headed for their debriefing meeting. The sighting of the two men from the plane that blew-up was logged along with the other B-17 that went down. The news from the invasion front was not good, as the weather had closed in over the area and all airplanes were grounded. The invasion troops on the beach would have to go it alone, or with only the assistance that the Navy could provide.

At the mess hall, Frank welcomed his shot of Scotch whiskey, his *Grog* ration, but he only picked over his food. It just did not taste right with the knowledge from debriefing that the two crews that had been shot down were from his hut. The crew that had been lost on Sunday had also bunked in his hut and he had known these men well. This meant that Frank's crew of enlisted men now comprised the *old men* of the hut. Four crews of 24 men slept in the wood and tarpaper building that was sixteen by thirty-six feet and was filled with double bunks. The exposed rafters and two-by-four walls were partly covered with *pin-up* pictures of Betty Grable that someone had cut from a magazine. Four bare light bulbs provided their only light.

As Frank sat in the hut with his crew, he knew it would be a lonesome night. Damn, what bad luck— eighteen men gone. It was a bitter pill to swallow, knowing that his new friends were now dead. The quartermaster soon came to pick up the men's belongings.

Frank's mind wandered, searching for better thoughts. There had been times since he entered the Army Air Corps fourteen months ago that were not all this bad. Some of his experiences had constituted a reality check for this teenager from the Blue Ridge Mountains of Virginia. Taking an eighteen-year-old country boy with a southern drawl and sticking him out in the world created a real shock to his upbringing. Life was certainly different from what he had known in rural America. Few if any of the country girls were as forward as the females he had met while traveling. It could have been the Lifebuoy soap he used or maybe his southern drawl, but whatever, it brought a grin to his face when he remembered certain incidents.

Frank had entered the service on March 19, 1943, and was sent first to Camp Lee in Virginia for indoctrination. From there, he went to Miami, Florida for basic training, and then to Gulfport, Mississippi for Airplane Mechanic Training. He turned nineteen on August 13, 1943, and when he finished mechanic's school, he was sent to Las Vegas, Nevada for aerial gunnery training. On the troop train en route from Gulfport to Las Vegas, in the town of Abilene, Texas, was where the incident had started—an incident he was never to forget.

The two combat missions today had required him to

breathe oxygen for a total of nine hours and this made for a slight lightheaded sensation. When he returned to the mess hall and received his shot of Scotch whiskey on top of his oxygen-saturated blood, it made him loose and he let the memories roll before his mind. It was not difficult to see in his mind's eye the event as he remembered it happening. He could almost feel the warmth of the hot Texas sunshine.

In Abilene, the train had stopped to let the troops off for some exercise and the troop commander put the men through a 10-minute close-order drill. Some civilians had gathered to watch the men execute the drill and gave them a round of applause when they finished. The officer then dismissed the men and they were allowed to wander around the station. Frank walked away and leaned against a support column of the station walkway, watching some young ladies walking toward town from the station. Someone tapped him on the shoulder and when he turned, he was facing a female marine lieutenant. He snapped to his best attention and saluted.

She put him at ease and told him she just wanted to talk. She said she was in charge of a troop of female marine recruits in the cars ahead of the mess car. The gist of her conversation was that she was unhappy with the military and she was lonesome and tired of dealing with the females and listening to their prattle. She wanted to know if Frank missed his female companionship as much as she missed her male friends in civilian life.

An officer had never confronted Frank face-to-face before and he was petrified as he answered, "Yes, ma'am. Ain't nothing like friendly company, especially pretty girls. I miss them a lot."

The lieutenant continued talking about how she regretted entering the service and wished she could get out with an honorable discharge. She told Frank that her car was just ahead and adjacent to the mess car, and that it also served as her office and bunkroom—her home on wheels.

Then she floored Frank by saying, "I've really enjoyed this talk, but I have to get my troops back aboard the train. I'd like to talk some more with you, though. Can you meet me in the mess car at around eleven tonight."

Frank saluted as she turned to leave, but she only smiled. The country boy knew he was one step away from putting both feet in deep *doo-doo*, but this was one meeting he intended to keep. The situation had tickled his imagination because not only was she a lieutenant, she was also a very pretty one.

He made his way to the mess car, arriving at 11:00 p.m. sharp. No one was there, so thinking it must have been a big joke on him, he turned to leave. Then he heard the door open at the other end of the car, and there she stood. The marine officer beckoned him to follow her. Inside the next car was a room to one side and he followed her into a bedroom/office. She closed and locked the door. Without saying a word, she popped the top on two cokes and motioned Frank to sit beside her on the bunk. He imagined he was one small step away from the stockade, but he sat anyway, sweat dampening his shirt under his arms.

As they drank the cokes, she told him that her name was Ann Hudson and that she had been fresh out of college when she began this dead-end job. She did nothing but travel back and forth across the country escorting new female recruits, never in one place long enough to make friends. Six months of this was more than she had bargained for and she was lonesome. Her idea of being a marine was not to mother a bunch of girls her same age, which was twenty-two. She wanted out of the service but her commission did not allow for discharge except for medical reasons.

Sweating profusely, Frank thought to himself, "Don't even consider it!"

Then he thought, "Don't be so damn dumb, Frank," as she removed her shirt and kicked off her shoes. "Oh, what the hell," he concluded.

He left the marine lieutenant at about 2:00 a.m. and slipped through the cars to his bunk. Sleep did not come quickly that night.

The next morning his traveling buddy, Bob, asked, "What's that cologne you have on? Hadn't noticed it before."

Jokingly, Frank replied, "I think it's called Military Brass."

These many months later, he still grinned at the memory. Taking his tray and dumping it, Frank walked from the mess hall into the rain, thinking, "Hell, it ain't such a bad day after all."

Lying on his bunk in the crew's hut, the effects of the oxygen and Scotch began to wear off and his back and neck hurt from the fall. The darkening bruise on his heel was painful, reminding him of how close he had come to getting a Purple Heart. Going to the base Flight Surgeon to have one's problems checked was, of course, not an option. The surgeon would no doubt ground him and he would miss flying with his crew. He wanted to stay with these men, as they had become his friends.

Other than what he had learned in his stateside training, Frank had not known what to expect on these first missions. Combat, however, was totally different from any lessons he had received. In his hometown theaters, Frank had seen war movies about combat flying, but here there was no background music and the blood and death were very real.

Mark, the top turret gunner, entered the hut and told the crew that because of the weather they had canceled all flying. The crew's plane was being repaired and should be ready when the weather cleared. It had received only minor damage when compared to some of the other B-17s that had taken a real beating. With that news, Frank got comfortable in his bunk and soon slipped off into a world of dreams.

Thus ended D-Day, June 6, 1944.

The next morning Frank found he had slept through a German air raid. Someone had tried to wake him, but he never became fully aware of what was happening. A lone German HE-111 bomber had slipped through the spotter network. No one knew how he located the base and found the ground targets in the rain. It didn't seem that the German could not have done it without help from someone on the ground, so something must have given the pilot a target. Rumor had it there was a spy on base. But who? And why? Why would anyone do such a thing? The Germans had spies planted in England, of course, and some were people one would never expect. Often they were women who could get soldiers to talk.

Blackout security was strictly enforced and every man was aware of what could happen if a German pilot found a target. No one was allowed even to light a cigarette outside at night. All windows were covered and light traps were installed at all doors. Frank had been told that a German pilot could spot the light of a match from twenty miles away. Flashlights were taped to give off only a slit of light, and were used only when necessary. A spy could, of course, place a flashlight in an area that could be seen only from the air. Aimed in a certain direction and left burning, it would be like a beacon for a night bomber. It seemed that was what had taken place to give this pilot a night target in the rain. This was, of course, only speculation, yet what other answer could there be?

The HE-111 bomber did not carry many bombs, but this joker had made every one count. The bombs had hit a gas tank and a parked B-17 located near the tanks, causing collateral damage to several trucks and other equipment. It was a real kick-in-the ass to think that someone associated with the base would put men and equipment in jeopardy this way.

The area bombed was only about 1,000 feet from where Frank was sleeping. Several men had tried to awaken him but the two missions on D-Day had zonked him and he slept through all the sirens, blasts and noise of men running around. A piece of the B-17 that blew-up during the raid fell some 200 feet away from where Frank slept.

For five days, the rain fell and the poor bastards on the beaches were catching hell, without one American airplane to help. All crews were restricted to the base awaiting the first break in the weather, as ground crews stayed busy repairing damage to the airplanes. There was not much for the combat crews to do but lay around and try to keep busy writing letters and playing poker. There was very little conversation. Waiting was the hardest part of this job.

Frank had time to think about his arrival at Great Ashfield and that first combat mission. Already, it seemed like a dream. It had been the night of June 4, and the sun had set beyond the field across from the 549th squadron encampment. The cool, damp English evening air had quickly swallowed the heat of the day. It had been countdown time for the airmen as all were waiting for the posting of the 10:30 p.m. loading list. This had created tension, excitement and dread for Frank as well as all other members of the crew. They had waited several days for the weather to clear so they could go on that first mission. Everyone questioned what it was like to fly in real combat.

The waiting was soon over as the list was posted and the names of Frank's crew appeared. The teenager from the Blue Ridge Mountains of Virginia had a grin across his youthful face as he headed for the hut and hit the sack. Going to sleep was not a problem since it had been a part of their training.

At 3:00 a.m., the CQ awakened them, making sure all were on their feet. The early morning mission was to Versailles, France. The target was a railroad-marshaling yard filled with trains. The formation of 35 bombers destroyed the target, but the anti-aircraft fire had been heavy. Fortunately, their plane had escaped with little damage. Unlike a dream now, it was more a nightmare as a crew from Frank's hut had been shot down over the target, the empty bunks serving as a reminder until a new crew was assigned to the hut.

On the night of June 10, the rain clouds began to break and the moon could be seen trying to light the night. The rest period was over for the 385th Bomb Group, and on Sunday, June 11, D-Day + 5, the crew was back in action early in the dark morning sky. The cloud cover had thinned over the Normandy beach and many airplanes were back in the air helping the invasion troops on the ground. The news was that the Germans were cutting the troops to pieces, with many soldiers being killed on both sides.

The weather had taken its toll by stopping the Air Force, so maybe this mission would help the poor devils down there. The target consisted of beach gun emplacements at LeTouquet in France. According to the briefing officer, German gun batteries had the American forces pinned down, making this a vital target that must be destroyed. The airplanes were loaded with twenty 250-pound bombs, which were heavy enough to break through the concrete gun emplacements.

At altitude, the outside air temperature was fifty degrees below zero, and even the fur-lined flight suit with other clothing underneath was not enough to keep Frank warm. Cold from the metal turret door drained away his body heat and he shivered. The rubber oxygen mask on his face warmed slightly from his breath, but moisture condensed and dripped from the drain onto his scarf, then quickly froze.

Scanning the early morning sky from his position in the ball turret, Frank could see that the clouds were moving to the southeast, away from the invasion front. He thought of what a muddy mess it must be down there after all the rain over the past few days. Up here, it was cold as hell, but this had to be better than fighting and trying to sleep in all that mud. He would take the cold over the mud any day.

Slung from underneath the airplane at 25,000 feet, he had a panoramic view of everything below. He could see low flying airplanes and naval ships blasting the inner shore positions. The Channel continued to be a beehive of activity. German defensive anti-aircraft fire seemed light, and strangely enough, not one German fighter plane was reported. Several flak bursts hit Frank's airplane, but damage was minor and no one was injured. Still, they had ruined someone's Sunday morning.

The return trip from the target was uneventful. Back at base it was to supply, debriefing and the mess hall for a shot of Scotch and then lunch. They spent Sunday afternoon catching up on sleep. Frank wondered why the Brass found it necessary to bomb a target at 9:00 a.m. rather than 11:00 a.m., robbing him of two hours sleep. The question would go without asking!

There were not a lot of things to do for amusement at Great Ashfield, and there usually was not much time, even if you found something you liked to do. Taking cold showers, playing barracks poker, letter writing and some board games at the recreation hall were about all there was to do. Some local British women usually staffed the recreation hall and they often brought their daughters along. Frank paid little attention to the young girls, however, figuring there was no need getting in a sweat for nothing, as the mothers kept a watchful eye on the young airmen.

Monday, June 12, Mission number 6, D-Day + 6. This mission was to destroy an airfield at St. Martin in France. The briefing officer said the field had been used to attack invading troops of both the American and British.

Most German airfields were just large grassy areas without hard tarmac landing strips. They could quickly set up a field by using farmland and adding temporary shacks for maintenance. That must have been the case here, as there were no flyable airplanes at this location, although damaged fighters remained from when the Germans had abandoned the field. Frank thought they must have known about this mission in advance, as this should have been an important attack field.

Neither was there any defense—no flak, nothing whatsoever. The 35 bombers were each loaded with thirty-eight 100-pound bombs and Frank watched as approximately 1300 bombs ploughed the earth below him. The field was filled with bomb craters and few buildings ceased to exist. The Germans would not be using this for an airfield anytime soon.

The return trip was without contact with the Germans and Frank sat and watched the beautiful scenery for a while. After crossing the coast of England, he, King and Alex sat in the waist of the airplane and smoked cigarettes.

The crew decided the old B-17 assigned to them should have a name, since most other planes on the base did. After much discussion, they selected a name to reflect the general appearance of the airplane, which was an older "F" model, with some modifications making it similar to the newer "G" model. The tail gunner's section had been changed slightly and a chin turret with two .50-caliber machine guns had been added. The waist gunners still had the full open windows that allowed cold air to blow in whenever the windows were opened in combat. This made for an uncomfortable situation in the cold skies but that was the way it had to be. Alex and King, the waist gunners, never complained. The old airplane had seen combat service elsewhere before being sent to the 385th Bomb Group. It was a faded olive drab color with many flak-damaged areas patched over.

The name they finally came up with was "War Horse." The old girl had served the crew well and so far, the only injury to the crew was the grape-colored bruise on Frank's left heel, which was still sore and caused him to walk with a noticeable limp. He carried the piece of shrapnel in his pocket as a souvenir, and as he fingered the piece of flak, it always reminded him of how close it came to ending his career as a ball turret gunner.

Frank had started with this crew in Dyersburg, Tennessee in January, some six months ago, when the ten men had come together for overseas training as a crew. All were strangers to each other then, and no two had come from the same state. The men were casually friendly toward one another, but willing to meet new people. When the list of names was posted, four officers and six enlisted men met as a team for the first time in the corner of a hangar.

The four officers were all Second Lieutenants: Lt. R. H. Silver, Pilot; Lt. A. D. Maxwell, Co-pilot; Lt. M. M. Butt, Navigator; and Lt. M. R. Slater, Bombardier.

All six enlisted men were Buck Sergeants: Sgt. Mark I. Rogers, Top Turret Gunner; Sgt. Donald R. Swope,

Radioman; Sgt. Frank R. Mays, Ball Turret Gunner; Sgt. Wayne S. Alexander (Alex), Left Waist Gunner; Sgt. Carlton P. King (King), Right Waist Gunner; Sgt. Wilber M. Koop (Koop), Tail Gunner.

During their three months of intense training at Dyersburg, individual training was honed and they began to operate as a team. Whether they lived or died now depended on each member doing his job, so the ten men on Frank's crew soon became compatible and developed into a polished team. When their overseas training was completed, all crewmembers were advanced in rank by one grade. The higher the rank of a soldier, the more the Germans respected him. The Germans frowned on any soldier having a rank less than Sergeant, so the new rank of Staff Sergeant would help if any members of the crew were shot down and captured. This also meant an increase in pay to eighty-five dollars a month.

With the training at Dyersburg completed, the crew received overnight off-base passes. Four of the members hitchhiked to Cairo, a small town in Illinois, where they did their celebrating in various bars. After a one-night shack-up in a cheap hotel, they returned to base, tired but happy.

The group consisting of 300 men—thirty crews in all—was then sent to Kearney, Nebraska, where Frank's crew picked-up a new B-17 and headed for England. The trip required one-night stops in Bangor, Maine, then to Gander, Newfoundland, and from Gander to Reykjavik, Iceland. In Iceland, Frank watched the sun set at 11:30 p.m. The top rim of the sun dipped below the horizon briefly and then came back up in the same place, staying out of sight only for perhaps about five seconds. It really was the land of the *midnight sun*. The temperature was about 20 degrees and a steady 20-knot wind blew constantly. All Frank saw there were windblown rocks polished smooth by wind, sand and time.

From Iceland, it was a one-day flight to a base in northern Scotland, where the airstrip was lighted for landing only after the pilot gave the correct code words when on final approach. Never in his young life had Frank ever dreamed of being in a foreign land, especially Scotland, which was the land of his ancestors, and he was awed by thoughts of being there.

The enlisted men spent the night in a horse stable, which was all brick and clean. Their beds were GI cots located in horse stalls. In the mess hall, Frank experienced the British custom of serving airmen a ration of *Grog*, or Scotch whiskey, after a day in the sky.

The crew left the new B-17 in Scotland and the aircraft was sent on to a base for immediate use, while the crew went to a final school on survival in combat. The enlisted men traveled in a train boxcar to a place in England named The Wash, where Frank learned the latest tactics to help keep him alive while in combat. The instructors were experienced combat veterans who taught him lessons in a ball turret operation using a dummy turret mounted on a wooden stand, shooting machine guns out over the mud flats that gave the place its name.

They watched more *propaganda* films in the mess hall, similar to the ones they had seen back in the States, only these were more violent, with gruesome pictures designed to infuriate the men watching. The idea was to make everyone learn to hate the Germans. The films included what to expect from the Germans if shot down and captured. Torture was used to make the captured men talk. They saw many dead and wounded Americans, some butchered, others shot in the head, and some slashed with knives. The captured films came from North Africa and Italy.

None of the crewmen wanted to admit their fear of being shot down and captured, but it was obvious by their facial expressions. Pictures were shown of people back in the States: women and children, old men, babies, the American flag—all the things for which the men were expected to fight and die. Freedom! Freedom from the cruel dictators that would try to rule the world.

After a week of training, the crew was assigned to a base and they traveled by truck the short distance to Great Ashfield, the home of the 385th Heavy Bomb Group. Once there, they were assigned to the 549th Bomber Squadron. This was where Frank now lay on his bunk, with six combat missions to his credit, realizing already that not many men lived through the required twenty-five combat missions comprising a tour of duty.

There was *no rest for the weary*, because at 10:30 p.m., the First Sergeant posted another list for Frank's next mission: Mission number 7, June 14, D-Day + 8. Another German airfield, but this time it was located in Belgium.

With a name for the airplane now, the crew used it lovingly as they spoke of the "Horse." Tested in combat, she was not flashy like some of the newer planes with their bright silvery aluminum. Although plain, she was willing to give of herself for the safety of her crew.

This mission seemed like a repeat of the one to St. Martin, but with one major difference: German ME-109s were attacking the formation. The crew of the Horse felt they were ready for the fighters. Mark, in the top turret, reported them first. They hit the formation from 10 o'clock high, five ME-109s diving through the formation and taking down a B-17 as they passed. The Germans made just one pass and then they were gone. Mark was the only one to get off any shots as the fighters went through. A second B-17 was hit and had two engines on fire after the attack. The pilot of that plane managed to dive and blow out the fires in both engines. No one could understand why the German fighters made only that one pass and then broke off the attack.

One reason more gunners did not fire at the fighters was that they had to be careful not to shoot down their own airplanes. With 35 airplanes in a formation, in the heat of battle a gunner could be shooting as the fighter went through and he might hit one of his buddies. It happened every so often that a B-17 was lost due to one of the formation's own gunners failing to stop firing at the correct time. There was often no way to determine if a B-17 gunner or a German fighter was responsible for shooting down a bomber. The attacking fighters were always blamed, of course, and no one ever disagreed.

Back at base, it was the same routine: supply, debriefing to tell of the lost airplane and what the gunners had seen happen, and then to the mess hall for a shot of Scotch before eating. The food, which was not all that good, was supposed to be a special diet designed to cut down on stomach gas. Gas in the intestines and every cell in a person's body expands at high altitude, where the pressure is less than the one atmosphere at sea level. Lack of pressurization in the airplane could cause major problems, as stomach gas tends to lock-up in the guts and cannot pass without great pain. To demonstrate this, someone once tied the end of a condom before takeoff, and when the airplane reached 20,000 feet, the condom expanded to the size of a football.

Pork was the primary meat served to the airmen, and their infrequent red meat seemed to be of the four-legged *horse* variety. Soldiers were forbidden to eat most food grown in England. The British collected human waste and used it for fertilizer on the crops, and the cattle were neither vaccinated nor inspected as they were in the States. On the base, the men who collected human waste from the dry toilets were known as "Honey Dippers."

June 15, Mission number 8, D-Day + 9. It appeared as if the *milk runs* were over and now came the long, hard missions. Today's target was an oil refinery located near Hanover, Germany. The briefing officer warned that this mission would be difficult, as German fighters and anti-aircraft guns defended the target—perhaps as many as a thousand guns. The German anti-aircraft weapon of choice was the 88-millimeter cannon, which was about as accurate as a country squirrel rifle. The range of the cannon was over 35,000 feet and the B-17 was limited to an operational altitude of 30,000 feet. For this mission, the Horse was loaded with ten 500-pound bombs and all the 100-plus octane gas possible—more now since newly designed wing-tip tanks had been installed on many B-17s.

Small flak batteries along the flight route were placing anti-aircraft bursts smack into the formation of bombers. The command radio was alive with the conversations of the pilots concerning men wounded and damage to the airplanes.

Then the German ME-109s hit the formation. "Bandits at twelve o'clock high!" announced Lieutenant Slater.

"They're coming through," Mark said as his twin .50-caliber machine guns began firing. "Going to the rear."

"Damn, he almost flew into us," King shouted.

Frank opened fire as he tracked the German plane to the rear. Koop, who was in the tail, had a sight on the same ME-109 and he started firing. Tracer bullets seemed to be everywhere.

"They're regrouping in front for another pass," said Lieutenant Slater. "Here they come again!" His guns were firing as he spoke over the intercom.

The Horse was shaking from the jarring of the machine guns, as thousands of rounds were fired at the fighters as they barreled through the formation. Frank saw an ME-109 going down with smoke pouring from its engine. Then he saw a B-17 falling in about the same path as the fighter dived into the earth. Another B-17 was falling back from the formation and parachutes began to appear as men bailed out of the plane. He counted one, two, three, and then no more parachutes bloomed as the B-17 exploded, pieces of the plane and the men scattering into the bright sky.

The German fighters seemed to have had enough and they left, flying to the north, and not a minute too soon. Then the flak from the Hanover defense opened up on the formation. Dense black smoke appeared everywhere as bright bursts of fire marked each exploding shell. A shell burst underneath the left wing of the Horse, but did only minor damage to the underside of the wing. The self-sealing material on the gas tanks had taken care of the small holes made by the shrapnel.

Flak suddenly burst in front of the Horse, causing the number 4 engine to blow a cylinder. The co-pilot quickly feathered the propeller as pieces of the engine and cowling ripped off and fell away. Oil streamed from a broken line.

The pilots were having a rough time trying to maintain position on the element leader as concussions bounced the airplane around in the sky. Then the bomb bay doors opened and the bombs fell away from the plane. Frank counted them and reported to the bombardier that all were out of the bomb bay. The doors then closed and locked.

The formation reached the RP, or Rally Point, where the airplanes closed formation for protection from fighter attack. No fighters were seen, however, and everyone wondered why they did not come back to continue the attack.

"Shit," said King as he noticed a flak hole next to where he was standing. "The bastards came close that time!" The piece of flak had cut his "Mae West" lifejacket. He added, "I hope we don't have to ditch this baby."

Alex chimed in: "A miss is as good as a mile."

Don Swope said, "Come look at the holes near my ass if you want to see close." There was a hole the size of his fist no more than six inches from where he sat.

Koop joined in with, "I told you the tail was the best place to be. Wanna ride back here?"

Frank had observed the bombs exploding on the ground and he reported to the pilot, "I think we missed the whole damn target, from what I could see." The pilot contacted the formation commander and confirmed that the bombs had hit only about 10 percent of the target.

With the pilot's permission, Frank crawled from the turret and opened a box of K-rations. It was frozen solid, but eating it was something to think about other than the damage to the Horse and the loss of lives in the other airplanes. He chipped away at the frozen ham and eggs with his knife, putting a chunk in his mouth and letting it melt. It was not all that tasty. While he sat there eating, he looked around at the flak holes near his ball turret. The holes ranged in size from that of his little finger to one as large as a basketball. The big hole was no more than a foot from where his head had been. He remembered hearing metal ripping when the Horse was in the flak area, so that was probably what had caused the noise. After he finished eating the K-rations, he used that hole to dispose of the ration box.

Somewhere near the Channel, the number 1 engine quit running and the pilot had to drop from the formation and join the other straggling airplanes. With two engines gone, the Horse could still fly, but it quickly lost speed and altitude. Once over England, the pilot said the crew could come off oxygen, so Frank crawled from the turret and sat in the waist with King and Alex, smoking cigarettes—not just one but several. Don and Koop did not smoke and Mark stayed forward in the top turret. There was no conversation whatsoever, as all seemed to be in their own world.

The main formation was long gone as the stragglers made their way to the base. The airplanes with dead and wounded landed first, while the Horse circled in a landing pattern. In the debriefing, Frank learned that one of the lost crews was from his hut—another six men gone; friends no more. Frank's heart was heavy with sorrow. He had lost track of how many of the men who bunked in his hut had been injured and lost over Germany. Although he really knew, he did not want to remember.

When the quartermaster came to pick up the men's belongings, no one said a word. The routine had become familiar now, and it was most unpleasant to watch as the clothing and personal items were taken away and sorted to be packaged and sent home.

The ground crews were busy repairing damage to the airplanes, which would require several days. During this time the routines got old in a hurry. Some men were satisfied to lie around in their bunks all day while others wrote letters home. The ladies at the recreation hall brought biscuits and steeped tea, but all the young ladies stayed clear of the men.

Alex and Frank conned a pass to go into the village of Stowmarket, which was about the size of Amherst Courthouse, a small town near where Frank lived back in the States. The size was all that was similar, though, as they found English villages far different from small towns in America.

The two located a pub and tried to drink the English beer, which was room temperature and flat. Neither of them liked it and their first '*alfpint* proved quite enough. A ground crewman had told them that if they wanted whiskey they should go to a certain house located near the railway station. It turned out to be easy to find. They were welcomed and both quickly recognized what type *house* this was. The several reasonably good-looking women who helped with the serving of booze were big bosomed and slightly fleshy, not the type young lassies Frank would rather have seen there. The women were easy to talk with, however, and they were not pushy. Alex struck up a conversation with one named Emily, and soon they were having a grand old time. Frank rationalized that the women were too old for him.

After several shots of whiskey, Alex had decided to stay awhile, but Frank wanted no part of this so he left Alex at the brothel and went for a walk on the village green. It was deserted except for two lads and two young lassies who were kicking a ball around. Frank stretched out in the shade of a tree and watched them play. They were having great fun at their game of kickball, laughing as if they had not a care in the world. He realized that these children had known nothing but war since they had been old enough to remember, and he regretted that he hadn't had a chance to play with friends like this when he was a young child.

Frank remembered a time when children were playing near where he was going to mechanics' school in Mississippi. He and his soldier friend, Bob, had gone on an overnight pass to the small town of Gulfport, which was overrun with soldiers from two nearby airfields. There were so many soldiers that Frank thought one could not spit on the sidewalk without hitting a soldier's leg. They then decided to hitchhike to a place they had heard about not far from Mobile, Alabama. It was a resort named The Edgewater Beach Hotel. Neither Bob nor Frank drank, but they went into the bar and ordered a mixed drink. It tasted lousy so they just sat and talked while looking over the finery of the bar area.

While they sat at the bar, a waitress told Frank that

one of the ladies sitting at a nearby table would like to speak with him. Never one to refuse the attention of a good-looking woman, he went over and introduced himself to one of two young women sitting there. Soon he discovered the females were on break from a nearby college and were staying at the hotel for the weekend. Frank then called Bob over and before long they were outside on the lawn playing with a beach ball, kicking it around similar to how the children were playing here now. That place even looked like this village green except for the Magnolia trees that grew back in Mississippi.

When evening came, Frank told the girls that he and Bob had to leave for the base, whereupon one of them suggested the men stay the night with them at the hotel. The girls then sneaked Bob and Frank up to their rooms, which were elegant with all-southern décor and large four-poster beds that seemed to suit the occasion. The rooms even had washstands with large bowls and pitchers, just like ones he had seen in pictures of plantations. It was almost like a scene from the movie "Gone With the Wind." Early the next morning when they awoke, Frank could hardly bring himself to say goodbye. He and Bob had then hitchhiked back to base.

The young English children quit playing and left, so Frank went back to the brothel to see how Alex was doing. He found his friend having such a good time that he had decided to stay longer with Emily. Frank thought the booze had apparently settled between Alex's legs. As Frank returned to base alone, the long walk and cool evening air felt refreshing and cleared some of the horrors of war from his mind.

When he checked in at squadron HQ, Frank found

that one of the duty officers had left a note requesting Frank meet him in front of the recreation hall. He thought this odd, but went there and did not see the officer who had left the note. Oh well, if the officer wanted to see him, he could just wait until later. Frank wondered what this could be about, as he was nearly certain it didn't concern military business. The only connection Frank had had with this officer was that the man had accepted some money from Frank to put in the squadron safe for him.

The next morning at the mess hall, breakfast consisted of wheat flakes and powdered milk, reconstructed powdered eggs, and powdered mashed potatoes. The flakes and milk were a soggy mess and the eggs and potatoes tasted like dirt, so Frank's entire breakfast went in the garbage and he settled for a cup of hot black coffee and a piece of toast with Oleo. Alex had made it back to the base late, and at breakfast, he looked as if he hadn't slept a wink. He sat by Frank in the mess hall and when Frank dumped his food, so did Alex.

That night the crew appeared on the loading list posted for the next day's mission, and at 4:00 a.m., the CQ came through the hut waking the men listed for this mission. Alex still looked like something the cat had dragged in, the booze having really done a job on him. When the briefing officer said they were going back to the same target as on the previous mission, there came a loud groan from the men as they realized it was Hanover again.

Mission number 9, D-Day + 12. The only difference on this mission would be that if during the bomb run they missed the oil refinery, the bombs would string across the city proper, which was a secondary target.

At 6:00 a.m., the formation of 35 airplanes crossed the English coastline at an altitude of 24,000 feet. Each bomber was loaded with ten 500-pound bombs. While heading to the target, the formation received some flak along the planned route. Frank looked ahead and it seemed as if a large black storm cloud was forming. *Whomp, whomp*, the flak burst underneath the belly of the Horse, causing the airplane to jump and jerk from the bursts as pieces of hot shrapnel ripped through the body of the plane. Frank kept his turret moving to help deflect the shrapnel as it slammed into the turret.

A few B-17s began dropping out of formation as they lost engines from damage by the dense flak barrage. Still, the airplanes continued on the bombing run, making every attempt to complete their assigned tasks.

Over the target, Frank watched as the bomb bay doors opened and he counted the number of bombs as they dropped. He looked down and watched the mass destruction as the bombs exploded on the oil refinery. The flak barrage lasted a full two minutes longer until smoke from the burning oil storage quickly rose to a level of 10,000 feet behind the retreating bombers. It soon began mixing with a layer of low clouds, changing them to a dirty gray color.

A while after leaving the Hanover target, Frank spotted flashes on the ground in front of the formation. In seconds, bursts of flak appeared ahead of them. He knew these flashes were from guns firing at them and it angered him to know that he could only sit and watch the Germans shooting at him. Making a few quick calculations as to windage and distance, he aimed his two .50-caliber machine guns toward where he thought the bullets would hit. After firing five 10-round bursts from his guns, the German flak batteries stopped firing. He watched and saw not one flash, and there were no more bursts ahead of the formation.

The formation of airplanes flew directly over the spot where the flashes had been observed and not a single round of anti-aircraft came from there. Frank always wondered if his bullets had anything to do with the flak batteries stopping firing. Maybe yes, maybe no, but in any case, he felt better having fired back. There were a number of straggling B-17s behind the formation but not a single German fighter appeared.

Back at the base it was the usual scrambling of airplanes trying to land without radios and with on-board wounded. For airplanes without radios, the signal to clear the runway was to fire a red signal flare. The special flares contained a double red burst and when a plane made this signal, the runways were immediately cleared and ambulances were standing by to race to the damaged airplanes as soon as they stopped rolling. Many of the airmen from this mission would not have to go on another, as more Purple Hearts awaited the dead and wounded. The Horse had taken some flak hits, but fortunately, none had been in vital spots.

CHAPTER 2

The Dijon Supply Drop

On June 19, D-Day + 13, Frank's crew bombed an airfield at St. Mere Eglise, and on June 23, D-Day + 17, another at Epernay, both in France, for a total of 11 combat missions in 19 days. Luck was with them and no one had been injured other than Frank's heel, which remained sore.

Many covered trucks began coming to the base and everyone wondered what was going on, as the trucks and bomb storage areas were heavily guarded and no one was allowed near them.

On the night of June 24, Frank was at the recreation hall playing his favorite card game, seven-card stud poker, while awaiting posting of the loading list. Tonight he had been winning until someone told him his name was on the mission list for tomorrow. Then it was off to the sack. "Can't win 'em all," Frank thought.

Mission number 12, D-Day +19. At 4:00 a.m., the CQ came through the huts waking airmen, who were off to breakfast and then to supply. With all necessary equipment for the mission, they went to pre-mission briefings. During the briefing, the mystery of the trucks was revealed. Along with this news came a warning from the briefing officer. He said, "What you hear in this meeting is Top Secret. After you leave this room, don't speak of what you heard. This mission is to carry supplies to the Free French Army to assist with the invasion of France. We also suspect we have a spy on this base, so now you are fully warned."

Rumors of a spy now confirmed, every man wondered just who it could be. The person would be dead in a minute if any man were to get his hands on him. The carping among the airmen concerning just who might be a spy indicated they were fighting mad. Before, it had been only rumor; now this was real. A spy for sure! Who would do such a thing to jeopardize the base?

The voices in the room quieted as the briefing officer continued. The wall was covered with maps pieced together, with red tape marking the flight route to the target and blue tape marking the route home. He announced the different altitudes the group would fly and described how all this had been planned to throw off the Germans as to the actual target location.

When the men left the room, not a single word was spoken unless necessary. Even at the Horse, Frank's crew went about their duties in silence. The wheels of the Horse left the runway at 5:00 a.m. and they flew into an ebony sky. Forming the 35 airplanes into formation and leaving the English coast required an hour.

The supply drop was located at Dijon, France, about 150 miles southwest of Paris. No one would have guessed the area of the drop from the planned route. The group crossed the Channel, and then just north of Amsterdam, they headed toward the German city of Frankfurt. Once to the west and past Frankfurt, they turned due south, as if the target were Munich. At this time, the formation dropped from an altitude of 22,000 feet down to 12,000 feet. The group passed Stuttgart to the east and again dropped in altitude. Now at 5,000 feet, they passed Basel and found themselves in the mountains. Another turn due west at the Saone River and the entire formation continued to lose altitude down into a mountain pass. Now every airplane in the formation was flying below the mountaintop, through a deep valley. The scheduled drop would be made in an open field at the end of the mountain valley. Fortunately, the weather was great for bombers flying so close to the ground. This was to be the first large-scale supply drop ever made in France for the Free French Army.

The group had stayed clear of the defense areas of the major cities and only light flak came near the formation, with no hits on any airplanes. They had loaded twelve 500-pound containers in the bomb bay of each airplane. Each container was bright aluminum and on one end was a canvas cover over a parachute. The containers were rigged to be dropped the same as if they were bombs. A dead-man cord would release the parachute a short distance below the plane, and then the containers would drop to earth.

The Horse was flying the *tail-end-Charlie* position on this mission, which meant they were the lowest element of the formation, thus the airplane nearest the ground. Frank, in his ball turret, was the man closest to the ground.

"Damn, this is rough riding," he thought. "Never imagined I'd fly this close to the ground." He was not more than 100 feet up as they flew down the mountain pass. The pilots were having problems holding the position as the Horse bucked and jumped from ground turbulence. Below he saw a small stream flowing alongside a dirt country road. The treetops seemed as if they would scrape the turret as they passed underneath him. Frank looked ahead and saw a house with people standing outside waving French flags. It seemed they were expecting the airplanes and celebrating the sight of them.

Out of the pass, over a large freshly mowed field, the 35 bombers arrived at the drop site. Green smoke flares marked the field, but no people could be seen anywhere around. At 500 feet, Frank's plane crossed the field, made a 180-degree turn, opened bomb bay doors and headed back across the field. The 35 planes salvoed their 400 brightly colored containers and parachutes. It was a sight to behold as the colorful parachutes made the short drop to the ground.

Some airplanes did not drop their containers, and others dropped but the parachutes did not open, resulting in many of the containers bursting open as they hit the ground, scattering supplies over a wide area. Suddenly people appeared from the surrounding woods, grabbing and carrying off the materials. The formation circled and made a second pass over the field to allow the balance of planes to make their drops. Most supplies were removed from the field by the time they made the second drop. Frank knew the containers contained military weapons and ammunition, along with many other much-needed materials.

As the formation left the drop area and started gaining altitude, Frank spotted a German troop train in the area, not more than five miles from the supply drop. Each railroad car was plainly marked with a Swastika on the roof and the train was headed toward the drop zone.

Frank asked the pilot for permission to fire on the train and, with his permission, he opened fire with both .50-caliber machine guns. Steam bellowed from the ruptured engine as the bullets raked the troop cars. The train came to a halt and many soldiers jumped from the railroad cars.

Excited by what he had just accomplished, Frank yelled over the intercom, "YES! One German troop train to the credit of a ball turret gunner. Bet your ass not many gunners can say that!"

The formation of airplanes began to climb, heading due west. Minutes later, they turned north toward the French coast. When safely back over the Channel and heading for southern England, Frank crawled from his turret. Now off oxygen, he, Alex and King sat back and lit cigarettes. It was a great feeling to know that the supply drop was complete with not one American airman injured.

CHAPTER 3

First London Pass

The supply drop at Dijon was a turning point for the Free French Army, as this allowed them to assist the Allied forces by disrupting the Germans from the rear. It also helped give support to the Americans that Frank heard were invading southern France.

The crew of the Horse was notified they were eligible to receive an overnight pass, the first since arriving in England that allowed them away from the area of Great Ashfield. They would have a chance to see some of England other than the village of Stowmarket. King, Mark, Alex and Frank picked up passes at squadron HQ, along with the condom kits required with any off-area pass. The pass and kits came as a package. Alex thought he might just want to stay in Stowmarket, but the others voted against the idea. Then Alex remembered how he had felt after his last Stowmarket visit and he decided he would go to London with the guys.

Frank remembered his one and only visit to a *house* back in the States when he had been sworn into the service on March 19, 1943. The Army had allowed him a few days to get his personal affairs in order before leaving home, which was limited primarily to saying goodbye to his hometown. He met a friend and they guzzled bootleg homebrew until late into the night when his buddy talked him into visiting a brothel on Fourth Street in Lynchburg.

The brew made him less than amorous and created an embarrassment, requiring an extreme exhibition on the part of his female companion—one he would never forget and one he never intended to repeat. It remained an embarrassment, even as he thought of it now.

There were many American and British soldiers on the train going to London. It seemed the British boys didn't much care for the Americans and had a saying that expressed their opinion. "There are three things wrong with the Americans; they are overpaid, over sexed and over here." The train conductor had to step in to prevent a fight from breaking out among the soldiers. Once separated, however, everyone settled down to enjoy the 90-mile trip.

The train finally arrived in London and backed into Paddington Station to debark passengers. The four airmen hailed a taxi and rode to the Red Cross Club near Hyde Park where they booked cots for the night. Several volunteers, mostly young British girls, worked in the club, and appeared gracious. One young lass caught Frank's eye as being different from the others. She was extremely pretty and seemed more reserved than the other girls. The small bib of her belted apron emphasized her mature breasts and neat waistline.

Frank saw a sign advertising Coca-Cola and used that as an excuse to approach the girl. "Would you tell me where I can get a Coke," he asked her.

She responded in English with a foreign accent, "Yes, come with me," and led Frank to a table in another room where she gave him a Coke. He turned it up, swallowed a big gulp and almost gagged. It was room temperature and flat so he set the bottle down and looked at the girl in surprise.

"What's wrong with this coke?" he asked. "It tastes like sweet water."

"The English do not like ice or carbonation in their drink," she said. "I am sorry, I thought you knew."

"I didn't know that. It's not your fault. It was just such a surprise," Frank replied.

That started a long conversation, which both seemed to enjoy, her speaking English with a Greek accent and Frank speaking in his normal southern drawl.

Frank finally noticed the talking had stopped and they were just sitting looking at each other. She broke the silence saying, "My relatives operate a nice restaurant and I wish you would stop by. I am there most of the time."

"I will if I ever learn the layout of this town. This happens to be my first visit here."

"Oh, I did not know that. You must let me show you the sights. I can leave whenever I want, so let me know when you're ready and I will go with you, if you like."

Frank was not about to let this opportunity pass and readily accepted her offer. He told the others he had found a guide and soon all five were off sightseeing. On the upper level of a double-deck bus, they visited Hyde Park, Buckingham Palace, Westminster Abbey and many other famous places before finally stopping at the Greek restaurant. Frank's buddies left then and returned to the Red Cross Club.

The girl had introduced herself as Nichole Karros, and later Frank met her relatives who worked in the restaurant. It was most pleasant getting to know these new people. Nichole and Frank ate dinner in the restaurant and then left to see more of the town at night.

It was near midnight when Nichole invited Frank to stop by and see her *flat* or apartment. They rode a taxi through the bombed-out areas of London on the way there and for the first time, he got to see the destruction caused by the German bombings. Nichole's flat was located at 13 Braithwaite Place, not far from Paddington Station. It was an apartment in an area of brick-terraced houses. Nearby was a building that had been bombed out some months earlier.

He found the place cozy. It was small and compact, with a combination kitchen, dining area and a bathroom complete with tub and shower. The living room doubled as a bedroom. There was no sofa; just several overstuffed chairs and tables with lamps. Heavy blackout drapes covered the two windows. The double bed was covered with a frilly spread of many colors.

They sat and looked at pictures of her family back in Greece. She told him that she was lonely, having been away from home for several years. She showed him a photo of an American airman that could have passed for his brother. He appeared the same age as Frank and had a similar shock of dark red hair.

"You shocked me when I saw you walk in the club today," she began. "For a moment, I thought you were him, but then I realized that was impossible. He was shot down over Germany last month."

She paused and Frank watched tears well in her eyes.

"I'm afraid I'm not a woman of the world. He was my only lover. I miss him so much."

"Maybe I should leave," Frank said, not wanting to disturb her more than she already was. He stood and added, "I guess I'd better be leaving. It's getting late and my friends will be wondering what's happened to me."

"Oh, please do not go. I'm sorry, I should not have said anything. Please stay," she begged, as she put away the pictures. "I would like for you to stay and let me explain."

"That's not necessary. I don't need an explanation," he said as he started putting on his blouse. "I'm sorry my visit here upset you."

"Why don't you stay here?" she pleaded. "Your friends will know who you are with. I'm sure they will not miss you as much as I would."

Frank had been trained to hit the sack not later than 11:00 p.m., and it was now way past his bedtime, so this sounded like a good idea to him. Sleeping in an overstuffed chair would be much better than on a canvas Army cot at the club. And if he got lucky, it might not even be the chair!

Frank undressed in the bathroom, and when he opened the door into the dark bedroom, Nichole was waiting for him. She took his hand and led him to the bed, kissed him and slipped between the sheets. The chair would remain empty this night! Neither the sound of bombs bursting in a distant part of the city nor the wail of sirens would bother him this night.

Frank had also been trained to rise early, so when the morning light of a new June day came through a crack in the covered window, he was wide awake. With no need to let the day start on a bad note, he kissed Nichole on the cheek. She put her arms around his neck and held him close, while he ran his fingers through her soft blond hair.

As the first light of day illuminated her smooth olive skin and revealed her curved body, he saw a Greek Goddess, warm and tender, and inviting. She smiled and pulled him to her naked body. He slowly caressed her firm body and gently kissed her, as time took a holiday!

After a hot tub bath and a cup of tea, they were off to the club where he found the other crewmen waiting. His friends were not all that happy, having slept on a canvas Army cot, but Frank couldn't have cared less.

They ate a late breakfast of tea and sweet rolls at the club, and then all five were off for more sightseeing. As far as Frank was concerned, Nichole was the perfect tour guide. He certainly would have followed her anywhere. He had found something that was missing from his life: loving companionship without complications. They had stayed awake late into the night, at times discussing their private lives and relationships with others. Their minds seemed to travel the same paths except that he had come from a poor family and her parents were wealthy. She had been trapped in London after coming there for an education.

Nichole had said something that tickled his imagination and he liked it very much. Once when he walked to the bathroom in the buff, he had switched on a small table lamp. Nichole had watched him walk, the soft warm glow of the lamp illuminating his body, casting shadows on the wall.

"Apollo," she had said. "My Greek god Apollo has come to me. He walks with the gait of the gods. I've waited so long for my true love."

Frank was never sure what places they visited that day, as none registered in his memory. He had eyes only for Nichole, with her Greek accent, wavy blond hair, olive skin and a face and body seemingly sculptured by some ancient artist. Her tenderness and sharing blinded him to all others. It was late afternoon when the other men reminded them of the train schedule. Off to themselves, Nichole and Frank said their good-byes. It was a miserable departure.

The others kidded Frank about Nichole on the return trip to Great Ashfield, but he didn't mind their ribbing. He knew they were simply jealous. When they left him alone, his mind replayed the conversations and events of the night before. He had told Nichole that he might follow the same path as Alfred. He had mentioned the name of her former airman friend not for her sympathy but for understanding and to avoid more pain should something happen to him. She understood the danger of flying in combat and was willing to accept him for whatever time they had together.

As the train rolled along the 90 miles to Great Ashfield, Frank thought only of his encounter with this Grecian goddess. This was something he had needed for a long time. She was a person who accepted him just as he was, with no thought on her part to criticize him. His background as an uneducated country boy from a poor family was not a factor in whether she liked or disliked him. He was a whole person unto himself, just trying to make it in this world. He was willing to give his life so that others might be better than he was. Not the first selfish thought was in his mind, she had told him.

Frank's father, an abusive alcoholic, had done all in his power to break Frank's spirit. The result was a lack of confidence around other people. On purpose or not, that had been the way of things in his life. Frank's older brother had abandoned the family and joined the Army because of their father. His brother had been sent to the Pacific within a month after the war started in 1941, and had not been heard from since.

Family life? What was that? There had been no teaching of love from his family. Frank had never heard the word used around his home, and he never heard any of his relatives speak well of his family. This had caused Frank to become a loner at an early age. It seemed his father was only concerned with his bottle of whiskey, and Frank and his brother had been whipped regularly at the slightest provocation. School was unimportant and Frank had worked every day after school until his father was injured. At sixteen, he quit school and worked full-time cutting pulpwood, during which time he became as strong as an ox. Even now, he sent home a monthly allowance to help support his mother, who had been his only friend in this world.

When the Army gave Frank an I.Q. test and found his score to be 160, they did not believe it and required him to retake the test while two officers watched. He wondered what was such a big deal about passing the test, and guessed they thought he must have cheated. After the second test with the same results, the testing sergeant accused Frank of lying about not finishing high school, and wondered why he wasn't sent to Officer Candidate School. Frank had not been an "A" student in school because there had not been time to study, but he had never failed a subject.

Frank's mother had instilled ethics in him, which did

not allow for telling lies, and he could not violate that rule. His father had moved the family so often that Frank never had much chance to make friends, especially girlfriends. He remained a loner and was very lonesome, but being away from home did not bother him as much as it did others, and he rapidly became the perfect soldier. All he had to do was stay out of trouble.

Alex was Frank's only close friend among the crew. They had discussed their lives many times and accepted each other just as they were. Now Frank had found another friend in Nichole. It was great, one male friend and the other female, and he thought that he could trust both. Being able to speak what was on his mind and not having to worry about repercussions was great. Before, he had always felt the need to be careful what he said, even to people he thought were his friends.

This brought up a question about love. What was it? Did a life mate have to be a best friend? Love involved sex in some way. Could one have a female friend and expect sex any more than one could have sex and expect friendship. Was this why people divorced? Perhaps they had not been true friends from the start.

CHAPTER 4

Back From London

The day after leaving London was a long one for Frank. Try as he might, he could think little other than Nichole. Finally, he remembered the officer who had tried to contact him earlier and decided to look for him. At squadron HQ, he learned that the officer had checked out on a pass. "Must not've been all that important," Frank muttered to himself, figuring that the officer could look him up later. The day dragged on until the mission loading list was posted that night and Frank and his crewmen found their names on the list again.

His bunk, without sheets and pillows, was just not the same anymore, Frank thought as the wool blanket fell over his body. Their bunk mattresses were made of three squares filled with straw and they used Army blankets as sheets and rolled blankets as pillows. After much tossing and turning, sleep finally came and he was dreaming of London when the CQ awakened him at 3:00 a.m. He could not remember specific events of the dream but had a good feeling as he continued to think of Nichole.

The cool, damp morning air during the ride in the truck to the mess hall with his crew brought his life back into view. After a breakfast of eggs over light, bacon, toast, pan-fried potatoes and hot coffee, it was on to their briefing. The airmen welcomed the good meal, as it came only at special times. The mess halls saved all fresh eggs for airmen scheduled for a combat mission. Frank thought of it as a "Last Breakfast."

Three new crews had moved into Frank's hut while he was in London and he decided not to make close friends with the newcomers, as it was too painful to see friends become statistics. It seemed almost as if this hut had a curse on it. Except for Frank and his crew, every man who had bunked in the hut since his arrival, as well as all their replacements, had been lost over France and Germany, while Frank's crew continued to survive their missions. He questioned whether it was luck or had something to do with his religious teachings. When would his time come to be shot down? Or was he being saved for something else? He felt his life on earth would be a short one. The dark, sore bruise remained on his heel as a constant reminder that he had knocked on death's door. He knew the time would come when that door would open and he would become a statistic the same as all the others.

Frank knew several men that slept in other huts in the 549th squadron area, and they also had been lucky. It seemed odd that some men went so quickly and others stayed around wondering when their time would be up. Every week there was a funeral service, but Frank avoided attending, as he would rather remember the men as they had been while alive.

Frank decided he would be cordial with all the new men, but he would not become friendly with any. It was too painful to lose so many friends, and the fewer men he knew, the better he could handle their loss. His crew had been lucky so far and he could only hope the good luck would continue. The men in his crew were his buddies, but of course, Alex was his very best friend. He hated to think about the possibility of Alex being injured or killed. All this ran though his mind as he rode the troop carryall to the flight line in the early morning darkness.

The briefing officer had said this mission was to take out an airport near Paris. The bomb load for this seven-hour mission would be twenty 250-pound bombs. There was a directive stating that no bombs would be dropped on any target in France unless the target was openly visible from the air, because the field might be heavily defended by anti-aircraft guns and German fighters. At the Horse, everyone went about the routine of making ready for the mission. When the airplane had been loaded, gassed, guns installed, checked and rechecked, the crew sat awaiting the green flare signaling takeoff. During this time, they told the officers about Frank's new girlfriend in London and they began ribbing him.

"How was it?" asked the pilot. "Anything different from the American girls? She didn't go Greek on you, did she?"

"I'll bet she was a real doll," piped the co-pilot, "Them Greek girls are real winners when they're naked. You must be a stud to take care of one of them."

The other two officers, Lieutenant Butt and Lieutenant Slater, remained silent. The enlisted crewmembers knew better than to push their luck and they also remained quiet, afraid Frank might just whip some asses.

Frank took it all in stride and added, "You horny bastards are just sorry it wasn't you. Come along with me sometime and I'll teach you a thing or two about women."

The pilots *walked through* the propellers to clear the cylinders and completed all other preflight checks. The crew hand-rotated the propellers. When the control tower fired the green signal flare, the pilots immediately started the engines. After preliminary engine running checks were completed, the Horse rolled off the concrete hardstand toward the runway. The uneven concrete and tar strips along joints made the Horse creak and groan as if reluctant to go.

As the pilot rolled the Horse along the taxi strip, Frank started writing on a piece of scrap paper. This was something he had begun on his first mission. He made notes of his thoughts and events about the mission. He also wrote about his private life. He wanted to remember the people who had come into his life, as well as how they had affected him. It was something to pass the time as the airplane climbed to formation altitude. When the mission was completed and he was back in the hut, he would place some of the items into his logbook of missions. His idea was that if he were killed or shot down, there would be a record in his belongings and someone would know what he had done along the way. He frequently questioned who would really care what he had done, though.

This day he wrote: Wednesday, June 28, 1944, D-Day + 22, Mission number 13. Going to bomb a German airport somewhere near Paris. Bomb Load: twenty 250-pound demolition bombs. Planned altitude: 25,000 feet. Estimated time of flight: 7 hours. Target defense: Heavy flak and fighters.

When he returned, he added the time he was on

oxygen, as this would indicate the amount of time the airplane had been above 10,000 feet. That length of time was also how long he was in his ball turret on the mission. Frank believed in details. Everything in life was important to him; every sight, every sound, every odor, and his reaction to all these things. Nothing escaped his attention. It was his life and life was to experience everything around him. Frank savored every moment. He imagined he had so little time to live, and he wanted to make the best of his share. For some reason, he was convinced his life would be short and he wanted to live every second allowed.

The formation of 35 airplanes reached their mission altitude, left England, and crossed the Channel. The flak started as soon as they flew over the French coast. Frank knew the invading troops had not made a lot of headway into France. The flak was not heavy but very accurate and a bomber lost an engine as the first few bursts appeared.

As the formation neared the target, German fighters attacked from ahead and high. The fighters came through the group of airplanes, taking a bomber as they passed. The Horse was shaking from the firing of all the .50-caliber machine guns aboard. A German 20-millimeter projectile hit the number 4 engine and exploded, blowing the bottom half of the engine away.

There had not been time for anyone to say a word before the fighters attacked, as they had been hiding in a cloud above the formation. However, as suddenly as they came, the German fighters broke off the attack.

As soon as the formation was in the area of the target defense anti-aircraft guns, the guns opened fire. The first burst near the Horse took off part of the horizontal elevator, and the torn fabric fluttered in the slipstream.

"You okay back there?" King asked the tail gunner.

"I'm okay, but we're missing part of the elevator."

"Thought you said it was safe back there?"

Just at that moment, a shell burst next to the ball turret, cutting away a large piece of metal from the lower fuselage and spraying shrapnel around the two waist gunners.

"Guess I'll keep quiet about being safe," said King.

The bombs were dropped as the flak continued. Frank watched the bomb bay doors shut and the planes regrouped for the flight home. The Horse had many flak holes but the number 4 engine had received the most severe damage.

Frank maintained a watch on the bottom of the airplane to make sure no fluids were leaking from the tanks. The crew had been lucky on this mission and no one was injured. The Horse had not faired as well, though, with one engine destroyed and a number of flak holes. The damaged elevator was making it difficult for the pilots to fly and they could not keep the airplane in the formation.

The *ver dammt* German ME-109s reappeared, attacking the formation, and noise of the machine guns firing vibrated throughout the Horse. A B-17 that had fallen behind was taking the brunt of the attack. As the fighters attacked the lone B-17, they came in range of Frank's ball turret guns and he was getting in some good hits on them. His guns were getting hot, though, and he knew he had to slow firing or he would ruin his weapons.

As if by some unknown signal, the fighters broke off

the attack. It was then that Frank noticed the formation was over the Channel. German fighters would not continue an attack over the Channel unless they knew the bomber was a dead duck. The defensive guns on the bombers had convinced the Germans they were not going to shoot down an airplane.

After the Horse crossed the English coast and dropped in altitude, the crewmen came off oxygen and Frank could leave the ball turret. He tried to clear his guns before leaving the turret but found them frozen tight. Heat from firing the guns had condensed moisture from the air and the low temperature had frozen them so he would have to wait until later to clear the guns. Now below 10,000 feet and off oxygen, he exited the turret and lit a cigarette. Alex was standing looking out the left waist gunner's window.

"Come here, Frank, if you want to see London from a different view," Alex said.

Off to the west, through the haze, they could see the vastness of the city. Frank stood and looked without saying a word. Alex must have surmised from the look on Frank's face that he was thinking of Nichole, so he said nothing. He just grinned.

CHAPTER 5

Private Thoughts

When Frank's crew had arrived at Great Ashfield, the tour of duty for all airmen was set at a maximum of 25 combat missions. Not many men completed all assigned missions because if they were not killed in action they were grounded from battle fatigue. Many men could not make it past 15 missions and accepted ground jobs or they were hospitalized. Flying in combat was not a *pie* job.

Frank had completed 13 missions and had 12 more to go—if he lived that long. He had accomplished those first 13 missions in just 24 days, averaging better than one every other day.

The crew elected Frank to paint the name of the plane on the front fuselage, a task he did not mind. He had come to like the old airplane and thought she was a fine Lady. She was different from most of the other planes on base and no one knew where she had flown before assignment to the 385th Group. She was a mystery lady— maybe Frank's Guardian Angel. The name "War Horse" really suited the general appearance of the faded olive drab color. She and Frank had both flown their first mission from Great Ashfield on the same day. They were two of a kind.

He gathered paints and not only painted the name, but he also painted a picture of a horse—an old nag blowing smoke from her nostrils. He was not such a good artist, but the men thought he did an all right job. It took a long time for him to complete the task, but fortunately, the ground crew helped by securing a scaffold and some rags.

The painting kept him busy but it also gave him time to do a lot of thinking. Here he was, still a teenager, with 13 combat missions under his belt. He had watched crews from his hut being shot down over Germany and France, yet he continued to live. What were the odds of that happening? Frank did not fear death; it was almost a certainty that he would be killed. That was the fate of an airman. It was the *experience* of death, the pain and agony of the event, that was troublesome. He did not understand death.

Here today and gone tomorrow, with some sorrow on the part of the living, but they got over that and went on with their lives. Frank did not *want* to die; it just seemed there was no way out because of the war. Everybody died eventually, anyway.

Another thing he noticed was how homesick many of the men were. Frank did not understand this at all, as he was never homesick. He had overheard conversations of the men when they talked of their *loves* back home. Wives and girlfriends seemed to be *loves*. He realized there was no part in these conversations for him. Everyone on the crew was older than Frank. The pilot was 26 and the rest of the men were over 20, with him being the youngest at 19.

There was his mom and dad back home and several girls he wrote to from time to time, but these did not seem the same as what the men were talking about. Some of the men had wives and one had a child that was born just after he arrived here.

Frank did not know what they meant by the term *love*. What was love? Best friends? Companionship? Why did people get married? To have kids! That didn't sound like love to him. Frank enjoyed the company of males where he could hunt, fish, drink a beer, cuss and tell dirty jokes. He also liked the company of girls and the pure pleasure they could bring. Their smooth bodies and warm skin brought real joy to a fellow, but they could also be deceiving, possessive and catty. Some wanted to *own* you as if you were a piece of land and wanted a marriage certificate just like a deed to land. There was no defense against these females. You certainly couldn't treat them the same as you treated men. When the men spoke of love were they talking about sex? Now *that* he could understand. But to get married and raise a bunch of kids? No way! Out of the question.

Frank was a loner. "Love 'em and leave 'em" was his motto! Was that why he was never homesick? He had never been taught any facts about love. Was that what he was missing? A female relationship that could be called love? Why this strange feeling about Nichole? Was that the beginning of a love affair? He thought she just wanted fun as did he, but somehow he felt a different emotion that he had never before felt with other girls. Maybe he was just lonesome. That had to be it—just lonesome, as was she. They were just good for each other while he lived.

Why did it bother him so much when some of his buddies were killed on the missions? He tried not to be close to any of the men other than on his crew, but it didn't always work out that way.

There were so many unanswered questions. He had to think this through, but where should he start? Back Home? His family had been poor and moved a lot so he never got the chance to develop lasting friendships. He had to work after school with no time for sports. He had quit school at sixteen. He had a brother with whom he had little in common. Frank worked with men much older than himself, and he learned about women from these older men. Tough, uneducated men had taught him about women, and they spoke not of love but of how to handle a woman. With his lessons from these older males, Frank knew only one way to deal with females. He was not aggressive, but rather a gentle—maybe even bashful—type, wanting only to please. His mother had taught him to use good manners. She had told him, "You can catch more flies with sugar than with vinegar." He thought this worked rather well as he dealt with the girls he met.

So, what were females good for? Certainly not love, but perhaps rather to satisfy the now raging hormones in the loins of this teenager. A romp in the hay every so often with no lingering relationships seemed what they wanted also, so why not?

All that made sense to him was that male friends did manly things and played the field for the company of females whenever it seemed right. Was this the reason he was never homesick? He did not have to rely on any one person and remained completely independent of all others, just being a friend while it lasted, whether male or female. Frank thought he now understood his relations with others and could go about being a good soldier, with no close relationships with anyone. Who would care? He would no longer be hurt by the loss of anyone—except perhaps for a little while.

Frank had never had a problem getting a date when there had been time. Sometimes it puzzled him when it came to meeting girls. Some were aggressive while others seemed to act the same as he. How about that female marine officer? She had selected him from among a crowd of males. Why? Was her reason simply to become pregnant? And Nichole, with her beauty, could have picked any male she desired; yet, she had chosen him. He was glad she had made that choice and smiled at the thought as he continued painting the picture on the airplane.

CHAPTER 6

The Gambler

Frank was returning to the squadron area when he met Lieutenant Swartz, the officer who had left the notes requesting that Frank meet with him. Frank snapped to attention and saluted. Lieutenant Swartz returned the greeting and told him to be at ease. He then surprised Frank by putting a hand on his shoulder and walking him to the side of the street. The lieutenant lit a cigarette and offered one to Frank, who accepted the smoke as Lieutenant Swartz lit it for him. His mind was running a mile a minute wondering what this was about, as it was most unlike what one expected of an officer.

"Mays, are you a gambler?" asked Swartz.

"Only barracks poker and latrine craps, sir," he answered.

"What about women?"

"Women, sir?"

"Yes, there is someone who wants to meet you—and the sooner the better."

"Have I done something wrong?"

"No. You've got it all wrong. This is a very pretty young lady."

"Who could that be? Have I seen this girl?"

"Take it easy. You have an open invitation. How about tonight? Can you make it tonight?"

"Well, I guess so . . . if you think it's the thing to do,

sir."

"Get dressed and meet me at the rec hall at six. And don't eat dinner because that's part of the deal. And don't tell anybody."

"Yes sir, I'll be there on time, sir."

The two men parted and Frank's head was ablaze with questions. "What the hell is going on? Why me? What am I getting into now? An officer and a pretty girl?" Most officers hardly wanted to give him the time of day. Why was this one so friendly?

At 6:00 p.m., Frank was spit-shined and waiting as ordered when Lieutenant Swartz pulled up in a jeep and told him to get in. The lieutenant drove through the main gate and saluted the guard without coming to a stop. Frank wanted to ask the lieutenant questions but waited for him to start a conversation. It seemed like an eternity to him before Lieutenant Swartz finally spoke. Since Frank was deep in thought, the voice sounded like thunder to him.

"Sergeant, this young lady you're about to meet saw you at the rec hall," Swartz began. "She asked to have someone arrange a date with you."

"Have I ever seen or spoken to this girl?"

"No, she was much too reserved to speak openly with you."

"May I ask where we're going?"

"You'll like this place. It's a country estate like ones you may have read about in school. She lives with her aunt." The broken sentences came rapidly. "Don't worry, I've made all the arrangements. It's going to be a great evening. You're one lucky young fellow, Mays."

The drive through the backcountry lanes was short,

as the estate was only three miles from base. If Frank had not been so uptight, this would have been a beautiful drive. In front of them suddenly loomed a brick wall with an open iron gate. Inside the gate was a long stone driveway leading to an ivy-covered mansion, which looked to Frank like a castle. Swartz drove through a covered passageway, then around to the rear of the building where he parked the jeep out of sight.

"Com'on soldier, let's get this show on the road," Swartz said as the two walked toward a rear entry.

A door opened and there stood an elegant looking older lady.

"Dame Metcalf, this is Sergeant Frank Mays," Swartz said, smiling.

"Welcome to my home, Sergeant Mays. It's a pleasure to meet you. I've heard so much about you that I feel as if I already know you."

In his southern drawl, Frank said, "Thank you, Ma'am. My pleasure."

Frank slipped his cap under his left blouse epaulet and followed Lieutenant Swartz inside the mansion. The surroundings reminded Frank of a museum. Most of the furnishings had to be antiques.

Dame Metcalf spoke, "Sergeant Mays—excuse me, Frank—I want you to meet my niece. Ashly, Sergeant Mays is here to visit with us."

A stunning girl, whom Frank guessed to be about his age, had stepped around a corner into the room. She was dressed in a manner that seemed to fit in with the furnishings. Her long dress swept the floor as she moved. Frank was so stricken by her beauty that he did not know if he was supposed to bow or salute. She was almost his height, with shoulder-length hair so deep red that it appeared black. Her high cheekbones and slightly tanned skin revealed teeth white as pearls, partly hidden by beautiful, alluring lips.

Ashly extended her hand. *Good*, Frank thought, *a handshake and not a kiss*. He was sweating under his arms, as his manners were put to the test as never before.

She smiled, looked him straight in the eyes and said, "Sergeant Mays, it is my pleasure to meet you. Please come sit with me while Aunt Amy and Lieutenant Swartz converse."

"Yes, you two run along and get aquatinted. Dinner will be ready soon," said Dame Metcalf.

"See you in a while," said Lieutenant Swartz, grinning.

"Would you care for a Sherry?" asked Ashly.

"No thanks, I don't care for wine."

"I don't like it either. Let's sit out on the verandah."

Frank suddenly realized this was all too pat. Why would someone of this stature want to meet him? He was puzzled by what was going on, but thought she was rather pretty. He saw her as maybe a Princess.

As Ashly and Frank walked down a hall, he thought there was something odd about the house. Its interior conflicted with that of the exterior. Where there should have been a passageway hung a large portrait. Where he thought there should have been a window there was a door. The house must have been remodeled, making its internal shape different from how it appeared on the outside. The inside seemed smaller than it looked on the outside.

When dinner was announced and he walked into the

dining hall, he found the place stunning. The china and heavy silverware shown like mirrors, dancing with glows from the many candles that lighted the room.

Frank was glad when coffee was served after the meal. The butler and the maidservant had fussed around throughout dinner, and the damn lamb chops—yuck! It was almost more than he could take. He despised lamb chops and the mint cream sauce, too. At least the coffee helped rid the taste of the lamb.

"Ashly, why don't you show Frank some of your artwork," Dame Metcalf said. "Lieutenant Swartz and I have a little business to discuss and it may take a while."

"Go along, Sergeant Mays," Lieutenant Swartz said. "I'll be back in a while. It's okay, I won't leave without you."

As Frank followed Ashly up the stairs, a memory popped into his mind. This place reminded him not only of a museum but also of a royal brothel. He was not sure why, as he didn't see any loose women lying around. It was just a feeling. At the top of the stairs, he turned and looked at the entry and thought the house he lived in back home would fit inside this one area. In Ashly's room, she closed the door and Frank heard the lock as it latched.

"You're in crap up to your neck now old boy," he thought, "What's next?"

Ashly said, "Wait until I slip into something more comfortable. I'll be just a minute. Take off your blouse. It's stuffy in here."

Frank slipped off his blouse and looked around the room. There were several oil paintings stacked against one wall, and an easel with a half-painted still-life picture. A palette with cleaned brushes rested on a table in one corner, all as if she had just stopped painting. The décor and touch of an artist was obvious to him. The studio— or was it the bedroom—of a female? A beautiful youthful female artist!

When Ashly reappeared, she had removed her long formal dress and donned a light summer shift. The sheer clothing revealed her natural beauty and she was gorgeous. The belt around her Victorian waist pulled the dress taut, revealing her bra-less breasts. Sure that she noticed him staring, Frank quickly looked back at a painting, which was just as bad, since it was of a nude woman.

"I would like to be a portrait artist one day," she said, seeing he was staring at her and glancing at a portrait that she had been painting.

"From what I see, you're already one."

"Thank you so much, but I have a long way to go before I'm really one of the better artists."

"I see you only paint women."

"That's because I can only get female models. All the men except the very young and very old are in the military. I really want you … Oh! … I mean, I want you to pose for me."

Frank caught the hitch in her statement and blushed. "I'm not much to paint. You need a suave, macho male.""

"I saw you at the base and knew you would be just perfect for me. That is, for my first male portrait. Please pose for me, Frank. Please."

"Well, I guess it wouldn't kill me to try it just once."

"Oh, good, you have made me very happy. We'll have to set a time and I hope it will be soon. I suppose you noticed I latched the door when we entered this room.

I do not allow anyone in here—not even Aunt Amy."

Ashly unlocked the door and they went downstairs. As they walked down the grand curved staircase, Frank stared at the inside of the mansion. He thought the rich wood-paneled walls with heavy drapes and marble inlays in the floor would be fitting for a castle.

Dame Metcalf and Lieutenant Swartz were waiting in the parlor. "Aunt Amy, Frank has agreed to sit for me," Ashly announced excitedly. "Isn't that great?"

'Yes, I'm so glad for you," Aunt Amy said. "Frank, you are welcome here anytime."

"Guess we'd better be getting back to the base," said Lieutenant Swartz.

"It was nice meeting you and thanks for dinner," Frank said as he followed Lieutenant Swartz out the side door.

"You did all right, Mays," said Swartz when they were outside. "Unfortunately, I didn't do as well. I lost my ass at the craps table, and in no time."

"Wanna tell me more about what's going on here?" asked Frank. "I think I know, but I'm not sure I'm right."

"You saw only the part of the place where Amy and Ashly live. That's the smaller part of the house. The women's and gambling rooms are twice the size of what you saw. I owe Amy money and agreed to try and get you over to pay a part of my debt. Sorry about keeping you in the dark, but that's how I thought it would work. You will come back won't you? If you don't, I'm in deep trouble."

"I guess so. Ashly seems like a nice person and she's sure good looking. I plan to keep my promise to pose for her."

"By the way Frank, that money I have of yours in the squadron safe . . . I'd like to borrow it from you to pay the rest of my debt with Amy. Will you loan me the cash? Just for a few days."

Frank knew this loan could get him in trouble with the military, but what choice did he have? This lieutenant could have his ass in a number of ways. He had done nothing wrong so far, but trumped-up charges would be easy for an officer who owed money and was hurting to get his hands on cash. He was in uncharted waters here and his mind raced to meet the difficult situation in which he had been placed. There seemed only one choice. The money was not what concerned him, but knowing his ass was mud either way he answered.

Frank concluded that he had no choice but to agree to the loan and besides, he did want to see Ashly again. Being around her and maybe even posing for her tickled his imagination. Hell, it could be a lot of fun and he would like to see more of her castle, too. Storybook images about castles from his school days ran before his mind and he liked what he saw.

With all that in mind he said, "Sure, why not! You must be a good gambler. I'm sure you'll make a strong comeback soon. I think there's nearly a hundred pounds in the safe—about four hundred dollars. Just keep track and put it back as soon as you win back some cash, okay?"

"You're all right, Mays. I really appreciate the loan. This will be just between you and me, right?"

"Yes, sir, I don't want to get my ass busted. You keep that in mind and I'll do the same."

Frank knew he had just made a pact with a devil, of sorts. He had learned that fraternizing with an officer could get him court-martialed, and loaning money was even worse.

The balance of the trip back to the base was made without either man saying another word. Frank's mind played with the sight of Ashly in that dress without a bra. Damn, she was really something, but he knew he was outclassed, as she must be a princess or some other titled person. Hell, maybe she did just want someone to pose for her. He sure wanted to find out more about her.

It was close to 2:00 a.m. when Frank slipped into his bunk. Sleep did not come quickly. The question concerning the officer's notes had been answered, but now he had other questions. Frank had not seen Ashly on base and wondered if she had really been there. He never paid much attention to the girls at the recreation hall, though. Was this all Swartz's doing? And if so, why? A high class brothel and gambling house? An officer deep in debt? What was he getting into? The people seemed nice enough, but he couldn't help wondering if Ashly might be one of the younger prostitutes.

The next morning, everyone wanted to know where Frank had slipped off to the night before. They thought perhaps he had made a quick trip to London to see Nichole. Frank dodged their questions and kept quiet about it. He was thinking of the two beautiful women that he now knew, each of them the type for whom men would die. He wondered how someone like Ashly had gotten mixed up with a brothel.

Back home he had met a few girls and had never had a problem getting a date. There had not been many, though, since he had worked most of the time and that left him out of the dating game. It was amazing what had been happening to him since entering the army. Some of the best looking girls in the world seemed to want him now. Maybe it was the uniform. It sure couldn't be for the lack of males. The girls had picked him out of a crowd and that made no sense to him. Grinning to himself, he thought, "Damn, that Lifebuoy soap does work."

Then he thought about Lieutenant Swartz. How did he fit into this picture? It had to be the money in the safe. Then it dawned on Frank! How many men had put money in the safe and were lost over Germany? He didn't have a receipt for that money. Who else would know who had money in the safe under Lieutenant Swartz's care, and how much?

Was this a scam that Swartz had been working and he just played it differently this time? Why was Dame Metcalf willing to pay to have Swartz arrange a date between Ashly and him? There were too many unknowns. Well, he rationalized, the money would be worth it if things worked out between him and Ashly. He didn't even care if she was a prostitute; she was the best looking one he had ever seen. She looked and acted like a real live princess, though, and he had to admit that he would really like to get into her pants.

CHAPTER 7

The Portrait

Frank had the next day off from flying and wanted to return to see Ashly in full daylight. The weather was good and the bike ride to her place was enjoyable. He hoped the overnight pass in his pocket might come in handy, assuming he got lucky. He did not think there was much chance of him getting anywhere with Ashly, though, because she was too high-class to bother with the likes of him. Still, he had nothing to lose by trying. Maybe he could at least find out more about the brothel and Swartz's connection to it.

It was July 4, which was for sure not an English holiday, he thought as he approached the mansion. When he arrived, Ashly was sitting near where they had parked the jeep the night before. He had to drop the bike on the ground as she raced to him and put her arms around his waist. Damn, that was a real surprise!

"I'm so happy to see you. What a great surprise!" she exclaimed excitedly. "You were on my mind so much."

"I've thought of you, too," he mumbled. "I have a pass and thought I'd spend the time with you—that is, if it's okay."

"Don't even ask, silly boy—you should know my answer."

"I think I have the nerve to pose for you, but it'd

better be before I change my mind. I don't sit still very long."

"Well, all models do not just sit—some stand, you know."

"You really don't want to paint a picture of a GI in uniform, do you? I mean, they're everywhere."

"Let's walk in the garden and discuss it," Ashly said, as she took his hand and started walking. They stopped under a rose arbor and looked into each other's eyes. Hers were deep azure and there seemed to be a question behind the pools of blue. He started to sweat, having thoughts of her in bed.

"I don't think talking will get us anywhere. Let's get on with some painting before I have other thoughts," Frank muttered. He could feel perspiration streaming down both of his sides, wetting his undershirt.

Without saying another word, Ashly led the way into the house and straight to her room. She unlocked the door and held it open for Frank to enter. In her painting corner, where the sunlight fell, was a large mounted canvas of the size used to paint a standing portrait. She locked the door, walked to him, put her arms about his waist and looked him straight in the eyes.

"I want to talk to you about a nude painting. Now what do you think of that? Do we need to talk?"

"What? ... God! ... No woman has ever seen me totally naked in broad daylight. I don't know if I could do that. I'm sweating as it is ... Let me get over this shock for a minute."

"You will make such a wonderful portrait. I just know it. I have already pictured you nude. I've seen you in my mind, so it will not be the first time I've seen you without clothing."

"But—but what if … you know what I mean … How can I keep from … Damn, I just might … Holy crap! … I can't even talk."

For a moment, Frank remembered seeing a young girl stripping before some men. She seemed to enjoy showing off her attributes and he wondered when she had first stripped before males. Had she been this uptight? He had overcome his fear of being naked in front of men, but could he do the same with Ashly? She was different and he liked her. This was a situation he had never dreamed of having to face. Getting undressed in the dark was one thing, but never before a female in the daylight. He took showers with a room full of men but never had he been nude before a woman. He looked at her and thought of what she must look like nude. He would enjoy seeing her strip, so why not do the same for her, he rationalized.

Crap! *Why the hell not*?

Never had there been a judge as sober as he was now. Ashly just sat smiling, as if she could read his mind. He could see she had placed her brushes beside the large canvas and was ready to start painting.

He laughed nervously. "You're really enjoying this, aren't you? My shirt is so wet I'll have to take it off to dry."

With that statement, he began what he thought of as a strip tease act. Sweat poured from his entire body and he moved a high-back chair to half-hide him from her line of sight. He looked around and saw no way out of continuing the removal of his clothes.

Off from around his neck came the necktie. He felt

steam rise from around his collar as he loosened the top shirt button. The buttons on his shirt felt the size of silver dollars as he tried to undo them. Turning his back to Ashly, he pulled out his shirttail, wondering if he really could continue removing more clothing. His mother had been the last woman to see him naked, many years ago.

He sat on the chair and removed his shoes and socks. Still sitting, he finished removing his shirt and hung it on the back of the chair. It was getting to the point he dreaded. Still sitting, he removed his pants, folded them and laid them over his shirt. The tee shirt went up over his head and he used it to wipe under his arms, then dropped it to the floor.

Ashly came to him as he stood. She put her hands on his waist and looked into his eyes. "If this is too painful, why don't you stop?" she whispered and walked away from him.

He was embarrassed standing there wearing only his shorts. Had there not been light, he knew it would not have mattered. With that thought, his nerve returned and he quickly removed his shorts. Then he suddenly remembered something his drill instructor had said when he was in basic training. "Suck in that gut and stand up straight, soldier. Chin up."

Frank stood there, *au natural*, as never before in his life. He was five-foot-ten barefooted, with a 30-inch waist, and his narrow hips emphasized his 39-inch chest, making it appear larger. His entire body was covered with a sprinkling of freckles amassed while skinny-dipping in the creek back home. His hair, a gene trait from his Scottish ancestry, was red over his entire body, which contained not an ounce of fat. Not overly muscular, but rather slim and trim, he was as healthy as a barnyard rooster. Army life had been good for him, keeping his physique ready for military action.

Through the open window, warm summer sunlight glistened off the sweat as it seeped from his body. As if the mansion were casting a spell of approval, not a sound came from within the room, as they both stood speechless, neither of them moving from their tracks. Staring at each other, it seemed neither wanted the moment to pass. For the first time in his life, he felt freed from the bonds of his teachings concerning nudity.

Frank wondered why he so willingly complied when she requested him to pose for a nude painting. Then his mind cleared and he remembered it was because he thought of her as a Princess. His Princess! His confidence returned and he stepped from behind the chair and walked several steps toward her.

Finally finding his voice, he asked, "Why do I feel so comfortable standing here in front of you, completely naked?"

Ashly walked to him without saying a word. Slowly she turned him around, allowing her hand to brush over his glistening body. She pulled him to her and they embraced. Then he closed his eyes and kissed her, realizing that the portrait would simply have to wait for a future sitting. He unbuttoned the back of her dress and let it fall to the floor. As his knees bent, she quickly pushed herself forward and he raised up with anticipated expectation. She took him inside her and cringed with a low muffled cry. Overly excited, and with loss of all control, he instantly reached gratification as they stood conjoined.

With tears in her eyes, she kissed him, stepped back and walked to the bathroom. His weakened knees bent and he looked down. On the waxed floor where she had stood, he saw droplets of blood. His eyes moistened, as thoughts of her being innocent had not crossed his mind. She had given herself to his lust. None of this should have happened this way. Yes, he had wanted her, but he never dreamed he would be her first lover.

Why had she allowed him this freedom? "What have I done to my Princess? I acted without knowing, without concern, and without control. It can't be undone and now she will hate me."

When Ashly returned from the bathroom, he stood beside her at the bed, shaken with regret for his actions. He said, "I'm so ashamed of myself. If I had known I would never have ... I couldn't stop ... Can you—will you please forgive me?"

The tears were now gone from her eyes and she pulled him to her. Kissing him, she whispered, "You have done nothing to be forgiven for. I knew what I was doing. Was it not I who brought you to me? You have made me so very happy. It was what I wanted and you only tried to please me. I should ask you to forgive *me*. I'm no longer a little girl. Now I am a woman—your Princess, as you called me a few minutes ago."

Frank could not remember saying those words. He had never been with a virgin before nor had the opportunity to learn about female's bodies, and it bothered him to think of what he had done. It had never happened so quickly, so why this time?

"Ashly, what if you get pregnant?"

"That is nothing for you to concern yourself with. It

is all right. I know, and you must believe me. My country boy must not worry himself. I am proud of your concern for my well being. None of my brash, arrogant male friends would have given it a second thought, and would instead have boasted. You are so kind and with concerns, as I knew you would be. Look at me. I am delighted, and you should be too. Please smile for me."

Frank had yet to learn to trust people. Should he start with Ashly, he wondered? She did not seem concerned about having lost her virginity or the possibility of her being pregnant. He began to rid his mind of the mental anguish as he listened to her. He knew he had been wrong and she was not a party to the brothel run by Dame Metcalf. What could be her reason for wanting him? Maybe it was simply because she liked him.

When Frank returned from the bathroom, Ashly said, "The moon is full and the night is bright. Why don't we go walk in the garden? I'm sure you will feel better. We'll play as if we're in the Garden of Eden."

She wrapped a towel around herself and let Frank put on only his shorts. Then she led him from her room along a dimly lit hall to what seemed to be a closet. Once inside, she shut the door and pushed on a wall that swung open like a door. She turned a switch and lighted before them a stairway going down. Inside, she shut the wall and with his hand in hers, they descended to a landing with a door on each side. Continuing down the stairs to a stone landing, they came to a heavy wooden door with large hinges. Ashly slid the iron bolt aside and the door opened into a stone passageway. Cool, damp air rushed from a tunnel.

"This place must be riddled with hidden passages,"

Frank said.

"Yes, the present dwelling is built on a foundation that's over a thousand years old. This house was over three hundred years old when Aunt Amy remodeled it. She incorporated all the hidden stairs and passages so she could keep watch on all the rooms. Be very careful. This stone floor is slippery with ground water and moss. We will exit out in the garden."

A string of low-wattage light bulbs lit the way after she turned a switch. He counted his steps and estimated they had traveled 200 feet underground when another wooden door appeared before them. She slid the iron bolt and the door opened into a small room filled with garden tools. Frank noticed the room was built into a stone wall below a large terrace. They walked out on the stone patio area and the mansion loomed at a distance. The side of the house away from Ashly's side was brightly lit, but he had to squint to see Ashly's balcony. Suddenly, he glimpsed what he thought was a man standing on her balcony, but in a second, he was gone.

"I thought I saw someone on your balcony!"

"You may have seen the ghost of Richard," Ashly explained, nonchalantly. "Others have reported seeing him from time to time. They say it's lucky to see him."

The grounds were beautiful in the moonlight as they walked among the rose bushes and shrubs in the formal garden. Then they sat on a stone bench and Ashly began enticing him to make love with her again.

Later as they walked away from the mansion, she started to run and as he chased after her through the garden, her towel snagged on a bush and dropped to the ground. She ran a distance before stopping and stood with the silver moonlight lighting her naked body. She was a beautiful sight and really did look to him like Eve in her Garden of Eden. He stared at her beauty for a moment, then stooped, grabbed the towel and ran from her toward the mansion. When she caught up with him, he was spreading the towel on the stone terrace. Out of breath, she stood in front of him and unbuttoned his khaki shorts as she kissed his chest.

They both lay on the towel, winded from the long run, their bodies reflecting silver-white in the moonlight, giving them an eerie ghost-like hue with shadows of deep gray. Then Ashly blocked any chance of escape by rolling atop him. Frank glanced up and spotted two military officers above them standing on a balcony, watching. They laughed and shouted, "Hey Sergeant, you're looking good. Mind if we join you?"

As he lifted Ashly away, she also saw them. Grabbing for the towel and shorts, they ran down steps toward the wall door, making a fast retreat through the tunnel into the house. He noticed Ashly was careful to bolt all the doors as they passed through the hidden passageways.

In her bath, he enjoyed washing her feet and she did the same for him. He sat back and laughed. "Bet we gave them an eyeful. Wonder if they recognized my butt?"

"I was embarrassed and I know you were too, so why do you think it's so funny now?" she asked.

"It just is. Holy shit! They called me Sergeant! Could they have really recognized me? What if they tell your Aunt Amy?"

"So why did you stop laughing? Is it no longer funny?"

He could see the impish smile on her face and knew she was ribbing him. He picked her up and gently placed her on the bed and lay beside her. Staring at her beauty, he wondered how he could have been so lucky to have her select him as her first lover. After all, he was an uneducated country boy from so far away. This seemed like a fairy tale—she, his Princess and he, her Pauper.

Frank awoke as the gray light of another English day lit the room. They had slept wrapped in each other's arms and now her smooth body sent shivers of pleasure over him. He decided to let her rest, thinking he was the luckiest man on earth.

Later they bathed and dressed. Ashly donned a stunning dress that swept the floor as she walked. He could not look away from his gorgeous Princess as she stood erect and held her head in that elegant yet normal manner.

What could she see in him? He had nothing to offer in return for her affections. He could never be a part of her life. Thoughts of the combat missions came to mind and he wondered if he would get to spend more time with his Princess. Could this be his earthly reward before he died?

They were having morning tea in the kitchen when Aunt Amy entered the room. "I hear the garden was beautiful last night," she said, smiling slightly. "The moonlight made the statues look alive, as if they were running about. Maybe there were young ghosts playing on the terraces."

Frank decided he wouldn't live to fly another mission, because Aunt Amy was probably going to kill him. The officers must have ratted on them, he decided, looking to Ashly for help. He could not face Aunt Amy, and Ashly had turned from him as he awaited the killing blow to strike him dead.

"I hope you two didn't stay in that stuffy room and work on the painting on such a lovely night."

"No, Aunt Amy. We did very little work. Is that not true, Frank?"

Ashly set her cup down, placed her chin in her hand and was enjoying seeing Frank break into that sweat she had discovered he produced, even in the cool night air. He now knew how a trapped animal must feel when facing a pack of killing dogs. He had no place to hide. Escape from speaking to Aunt Amy was impossible and he did not know what to say. It was as if he had again lost the ability to speak. Yet, he knew he had to say something, anything.

"I've thoroughly enjoyed my visit, Aunt Amy," he stuttered, avoiding eye contact. "Ashly kept us busy and I think you have a very beautiful home." He really wished he could disappear from the face of the earth. Sweat poured from under his arms and Ashly remained silent, smiling at his dilemma.

The cook had finished preparing breakfast and placed a bowl of preserves and toast on the table. Frank quickly spread a piece of toast with preserves and took a large bite so he wouldn't have to say another word. There was not enough tea in the world to wash the dryness from his mouth as he tried to swallow the mouthful of bread. The toast and jam knotted in his stomach and it hurt like hell.

Charles, the butler entered the room and spoke to Aunt Amy in a low voice. Then the two of them left the room and Frank felt as if a heavy burden had been lifted from him and he relaxed slightly.

"I guess you noticed Aunt Amy knows and approves of our romp in the garden. I had to let you face her alone. You do not know it but she really is your friend. You were so sweet when you blushed. Your nice personality came through. You are so charming and so unlike the other young men that we know. You were the correct choice for me and I love you for being just that. When you started to sweat I knew you would be just fine."

Leaving the kitchen, Ashly led Frank on a full tour of the mansion. It was filled with paintings, suits of armor, marble statues, the finest of woods with carvings and ornate gold trim everywhere. Not once did she make a move to enter the side of the house where there was gambling and other activities.

After one last encounter with his Princess in one of the small hidden anterooms, Frank decided he trusted her, and any misgivings he had began to evaporate.

CHAPTER 8

Mission Number 14

Frank spent that night and most of the following day, the full time his pass allowed, with Ashly. When leaving, he had promised to come back to see her as soon as possible. As he had not eaten a full meal since breakfast the day before, he stopped by the mess hall on base. He wished he hadn't had to return, but there was the possibility his name would come up on tonight's loading list for a mission tomorrow. After eating, he picked up a towel and stopped by the bathhouse for a cold shower. He was ready to take on the Germans, or anyone else for that matter.

He waited around the entire next day before his name appeared on the mission list. On the night of July 6, he saw his name and thought, "Damn, an entire day of my life wasted. I could've been with Ashly all this time."

The Horse was loaded with thirty-eight 100-pound bombs and the bombers were headed for Merseburg, deep in Germany. At 25,000 feet, it was cold as hell. The P-51 fighter escort had just left the formation of B-17 bombers to return to England. The escort had been with them from the Channel to a point fifty miles into Germany. They had not encountered any German fighters and the flak had been light, as the flight path had been planned to avoid major cities.

"Bandits at twelve o'clock high!" reported the

bombardier.

"Coming through!" yelled Mark.

Frank made ready his guns and watched for the fighters to come below the Horse where he could get off some shots. The airplane resounded with the noise from the top turret and waist gunners as they fired at the ME-109s. Empty .50-caliber shell casings from the nose turret pummeled the ball turret and kept Frank moving it. Bombardiers and navigators were notoriously poor gunners, a fact well known to the Germans, which was why they usually elected to strike the formation from the front. They also had learned to avoid the ball turret gun position, if possible.

As the fighters went to the rear and low of the formation, Frank commenced firing. He saw one ME-109 blow apart and a second spiraling toward the earth. Then a B-17 from above came down and under the Horse, trailing smoke from two of its engines. As Frank watched for parachutes to leave the airplane, it blew apart and started down in a flat spiral, missing one wing. He did not see a single parachute coming from the airplane. Another ten men lost.

The target was ahead and dense flak began to rip at the Horse. Smoke from the bursting shells thickened to a black cloud. A B-17 drifted back and below Frank's position, and as he was looking at it, the airplane received a direct hit in the bomb bay, causing all 38 bombs to explode at once. Pieces of debris scattered in all directions as he watched the ball turret separate from the trash and plummet earthward. He knew the man inside did not have a parachute. *Gott im Himmel*. He could watch no longer. He spun the turret from the sight.

A shell suddenly burst in front of the turret with a flash of blinding red light. The bulletproof glass between his feet crumpled and burst inside the turret, sending pieces of shrapnel and glass throughout. The sound of the bursting shell temporarily deafened him and acrid smoke was stifling as it mixed with his oxygen. The ball turret had been put out of commission and would no longer operate by using the hand controls. Although glass and debris had sprayed all over Frank, not a single piece had cut him!

"How the hell did that happen?" he wondered. "Just dumb-ass luck, I guess. What a mess!"

He could tell that the electrical system had been knocked out and the turret would not move. He did not hear anyone saying anything but that was not unusual at this point in the mission. The same burst of flak had exploded a wind deflector board, located just to the rear of the turret inside the airplane fuselage. He could see a large hole just behind the turret in the bottom of the Horse.

Frank hand-cranked the turret enough so he could get into the plane, and when he opened the door, Alex stood there cursing because Frank hadn't answered his call on the intercom. What Alex did not know was that the shell had ruined his intercom system in the turret. Alex was terribly upset, thinking Frank was dead because he had not answered right away. It had taken Frank a minute to collect himself before cranking up the turret.

A second burst of flak had hit the number 2 engine at the same time as the one damaged the turret and oil was spraying over the now useless ball turret. Alex helped Frank pick pieces of broken glass from his fur-lined flight suit. Fortunately, none had touched his skin.

The German fighters had all gone now; Alex said they left the formation just before the flak hit. The group of airplanes had taken a beating and just how many were shot down would have to be clarified in the debriefing back at base.

Frank hand rolled the turret in the stored position and sat in the waist. He ripped his oxygen mask from his face and it hurt like hell where it had frozen to his skin. He held the mask to one side and lit a cigarette, wondering how all that damage had taken place and he hadn't even gotten a scratch.

The flight back to the Channel was routine, without any German fighters attacking. Again, Frank thanked his Guardian Angel as he surveyed the damage in and around the turret. The wind deflector board was strewn throughout the fuselage and his parachute had been ruined by a piece of aluminum from the fuselage floor. The metal had sliced through the canvas cover and stuck deep into the silk fabric, rendering it useless. Just to the rear of the turret was a hole in the bottom of the plane big enough for a man to crawl through. The wind coming through this hole was freezing as it drafted out the open waist gunner's windows, which they could not close while in combat.

Frank went into the radio room and plugged in his oxygen and intercom. He felt useless not being able to operate his turret. It occurred to him that if the airplane went down, he did not have a parachute. With nothing to do but listen to the intercom, he began to think of all the things that had happened in the past few days; it was certainly better than thinking about his narrow escape from death.

Never before had he had two good-looking women at one time, with both of them liking him a lot. They had almost lost him on this mission, yet his Guardian Angel had again been there to save the day. He would never tell Nichole how close she came to losing another beau. His thoughts then turned to Ashly and what a beautiful woman she was. He wondered whether she had made any charcoal sketches of him from memory. She certainly had seen enough of him! How in hell did he have that much nerve to undress before her? He had to be some kind of nut to pull that stunt, but still, the rewards had been well worth it.

Although he still had many unanswered questions concerning why she had selected him, he decided that now was not the best time to seek the answers.

CHAPTER 9

Lieutenant M. M. Butt, KIA.

Saturday, July 8, 1944, Mission number 15, D-Day + 32. Target: Robot Bomb Depot. Location: Near Paris. Bomb Load: six 1000-pound bombs. Altitude: 22,000 feet. The briefing officer said the depot had been identified by S-2 Intelligence as Hitler's storage area for Germany's latest secret weapon, which was either a flying bomb or a new type rocket. They expected the target to be defended by many anti-aircraft guns.

The crew was expecting to fly a different airplane on this mission but to their surprise, the Horse had been repaired overnight and was ready to go. Frank could not understand how so much work could be accomplished in such a short time, although this airplane had a great ground crew and the best grease monkeys.

The heavy load was almost more than the Horse could lift off the ground, requiring the pilot to bounce the airplane three times going down the runway before it became airborne. The wheels left the runway at 4:00 a.m. sharp and the Horse complained as the pilots coaxed her to formation altitude. In the east, the early summer sun was beginning to light the sky with shades of gold through wispy clouds. Back to the west where Frank turned the ball turret, the last stars twinkled like diamonds in the fading night sky.

He now thought of both Nichole and Ashly, his two beautiful women. One had hair the color of the sun and the other reminded him of Poe's raven. Here he was in the middle, and what a nice place to be. Yes, they were two more good reasons to fight a war. He smiled to himself under his oxygen mask, thinking that life had certainly become more interesting for him since arriving in England—in so many ways.

Frank was shaken from his dream world back to reality as flak started bursting beneath the turret when the airplane flew over a large anti-aircraft gun emplacement. The briefing officer had failed to point this one out in their briefing. Suddenly, the plane on the Horse's left wing took a hard hit and fell from formation with two engines shot out. It made a turn and headed back toward the base alone, but Frank doubted it would make it, as the plane was losing altitude fast.

The flak stopped as quickly as it had started, which seemed odd because the formation was still in range of their guns. Frank had spotted the location by the flashes as they fired. The lone B-17 disappeared from Frank's sight as it flew into low clouds.

Off in the distant haze he could see the outline of the city of Paris. There was a layer of scattered clouds over the entire area and Frank remembered the directive not to bomb in France unless the target was clearly visible.

The formation crossed the IP and started the bomb run, but a layer of clouds obscured the target and the bombs were not dropped. Odd! There was not a single burst of flak as the planes flew over the target. Not one shell burst as the formation turned and headed back on course. Where was all the defense about which the briefing officer had warned?

Off at 9 o'clock, several bursts of flak appeared dead

level with the formation, but nearly a half mile away.

"Ha, missed us that time. Not today!" Frank thought.

That thought had not cleared Frank's mind when the first anti-aircraft shell burst just a few feet away from the right side of the Horse's nose. The airplane bucked as if it really were a horse. Instantly at the crack of the bursting shell, the navigator let out a blood-chilling scream over the intercom. There was no way for Frank to help him as the Horse rolled up with a sudden jerk, pinning him to the side of the ball turret.

A second shell then burst underneath the right wing out near the tip and rolled the Horse up 45 degrees as the bomb bay doors opened and locked in that position.

The third shell went through the number 3 fuel tank in the right wing, just behind the engine exhaust. The airplane continued to roll up to a 60-degree angle and all six bombs were thrown from the bomb bay.

The fourth shell burst beside the ball turret, casting shrapnel into the belly of the plane.

The fifth shell exploded adjacent to the left waist gunner's window, ripping out pieces of the fuselage.

The airplane continued to roll until it was upside down and headed into a spiraling nosedive, throwing everyone in the airplane about and gluing Frank to his seat in the ball turret.

The navigator continued to scream over the intercom, pleading, "For God's sake, please someone help me . . . I've been hit."

Gas gushed from the hole in the tank and found its way inside the plane to the bomb bay, pouring back onto Frank's ball turret and beginning to mix with his oxygen. The ball turret was positioned so that Frank could have gotten into the airplane, but he couldn't move due to the "g" forces. From the turret, he could now see only blue sky.

Lieutenant Butt continued to scream for help as the airplane rolled into a vertical spin and fell from 22,000 down to 10,000 feet. After about a minute, the pilots managed to pull out from the dive and level off, but the plane was still headed down.

Mark and the bombardier finally got to Lieutenant Butt and cut away his clothing trying to get at the wounds and stop the flow of blood. Lieutenant Butt still had control of his mike switch and would not let it go as he continued to scream. Koop crawled from the tail gunner's position and all except Frank snapped on parachutes. Frank went forward to assist with Lieutenant Butt, who continued to scream. He cut away more clothing, fully exposing the many wounds. A piece of shrapnel had entered Lieutenant Butt's hip, hit a bone and splintered up into his intestines, exiting in several places. Compress bandages were applied and a tube of morphine injected, but with little effect.

Blood flowed from the wounds and puddled on the deck. Lieutenant Butt continued to scream, pleading for help to stop the pain. The four airmen were covered with blood as it squirted when a bandage slipped. Mark injected the second tube of morphine with little apparent effect on Lieutenant Butt's pain. As he lost blood, he began to struggle less, but he screamed for more morphine and Mark gave him the third injection. In a few minutes, he began to drift in and out of consciousness and the blood pressure gauge began to register dangerously low.

All of Frank's stateside emergency training had been

put to use and he still felt as if he were failing his friend, as Lieutenant Butt grew weak and tried to speak. He looked Frank in the eyes and said, "Give 'em hell boys . . . I'm done for." Then he spoke no more. The flight to base was finished in silence as bloody hands held bandages to the lieutenant's wounds.

At the base, the crew rode to the hospital and when the flight surgeon pronounced Lieutenant Butt dead, the men were allowed to wash up and go to debriefing. No one was yet able to relate the series of events, so they were told to report back two hours after eating. No one felt like eating, but Frank and the others welcomed their shot of Scotch. Frank wished he could have drunk the whole bottle.

At the later debriefing, they were told that a funeral would be held on Monday at the Cambridge Military Cemetery and Lieutenant Butt would be interred at that time.

On Sunday morning, the entire crew went to the flight line to see the airplane. The damage was extensive and the ground crew estimated there were more than 250 flak holes in the Horse, ranging in size from a pencil to one big enough for a man to crawl through. The biggest hole was through the gas tank and all were at a loss as to why the airplane had not blown apart. The exhaust from the number 3 engine had been burning into the gas as it poured from the hole in the wing and tank. The oxygen system had been damaged and all oxygen had been lost, although no one had even noticed in the heat of battle. Mark had been forced to hand-crank the wheels down because the hydraulic system had been shattered after losing all the fluid.

With the hydraulics gone and no brakes to stop the roll of the airplane, King and Alex, with the help of Koop, had rigged a parachute to the tail wheel strut. Once the wheels were on the runway, Koop tossed the chute out his escape hatch. The parachute bloomed open, then ripped off from the force of the wind, but it slowed the airplane some. The reduced speed allowed the pilots to spin the plane at the end of the runway, saving them all, as there was a sunken road near the end of the strip that had claimed many lives on planes that failed to stop. It was later reported that they were the first crew to rig a parachute to help brake an airplane on landing. The procedure was investigated and placed in the pilot's manual for airplanes with damaged hydraulic systems.

After eating, the rest of the crew went to their hut. Frank was having a problem coping with his grief and needed help, so he rode his bike to Ashly's house, spending some of his emotions with the effort. He thought he had never seen a woman so stunningly beautiful as Ashly. She must have sensed his problem and greeted him with open arms. Her care and touch brought tears to his eyes, which he tried to hide.

They sat on the grass and she pulled his head into her lap. He lay there a long while staring at the sky as she traced her slender fingers over the contours of his face. She bent over, kissed his lips, then asked, "Would you like to see what goes on in the other side of the house? I know a way to look without entering."

Frank felt this was just the diversion he needed to take his mind off the death of Lieutenant Butt. Having questioned what went on over there, he quickly responded, "Yes, let's go look."

They headed up the grand front stairs to a landing where Ashly stopped and put her finger to her lips. She unlocked a hidden door in the cherry wood-paneled wall and led him into a small room. After she shut the door, it was pitch-black until she pulled aside a small drape over a slot in the wall and motioned him to look.

Through the small slot, Frank could see a gambling room filled with blackjack and other card tables. At one table, he saw several British and American officers playing cards. Dame Metcalf was playing poker with the *boys* and had the biggest pile of chips in front of her. The room reminded Frank of a gambling casino he had seen back in Mississippi. Blue smoke floated in layers around the tables.

Then Ashly closed that drape, opened another and they were now looking into a large bedroom filled with fine furniture. On the bed were a man and woman in a compromising position. As their groans and uttering drifted to his ears, he looked at Ashly and nodded for her to close the drape, as he had seen all he wanted to see. The man was Lieutenant Swartz, who owed surely more than a gambling debt, and this was one he could not win back so easily. Frank imagined the lieutenant was spending his money and enjoying every shilling.

After they left the small room and returned to Ashly's room, Frank said, "I'm in the dark about several things. Okay if I ask you some questions?"

"Sure, go ahead and ask."

"I hardly know where to begin. My meeting you, was it . . ."

"Let me tell you a little and then you can ask more if you like. Aunt Amy and I saw you at the base and we inquired as to your military records. I never saw them, but she did and was well pleased with you. She agreed you would be good company for me and I liked you from the beginning. Perhaps as you Americans say, it was *love at first sight*. Aunt Amy brought Lieutenant Swartz in on this because he owes her a lot of money. He made all the arrangements. I know it was not nice of us, but I really wanted you and Aunt Amy thought you were just right. I would never take part in what you saw a few minutes ago. Never! I cannot stand the other young men I know. And I really do want to paint your portrait so I will be able to see you forever. It will give me such pleasure to look upon it when I grow old. You are very special to me."

Frank thought the painting might be a good idea, as someone would then remember him when he was gone. In his business, one could never count on being allowed to grow old.

"I guess that answers most of my questions," he said, "but I'm embarrassed by your comments about me. The other questions concerned Swartz and why he acted toward me as he did. Now I see that he is one strung-out officer who is headed for real trouble."

Frank did not want to talk to Ashly about Lieutenant Butt at this time, as it would only upset him again so he stood with his thoughts until Ashly broke the silence.

"Anything else you want to ask?"

"I think I know enough to get me hanged if I'm not careful. So enough of that! Let's get back to your artwork."

"You really are interested in my art and not just me? That makes me very happy. I was afraid you would take your pleasure and I'd never see you again."

"Not a chance!"

"Here, look at my sketch. I keep it covered because it is just for our eyes only."

Ashly uncovered the large canvas, revealing a charcoal sketch of what she had remembered during her first attempt to draw him.

"I see you remembered certain things better than others," Frank said, and laughed out loud. "Haven't you overdone it?"

"It's not just the small things in life that always matter." She laughed with him.

"Want another session now?" asked Frank.

"Posing or otherwise?"

"Why not both? It worked before."

"See, you know what a woman wants and you cannot see it because of the way you are. I love my American country boy."

This time Frank had no trouble undressing in front of Ashly. It seemed the right thing to do as his teachings of nudity took a back seat. Then he watched from the corner of his eye as his Princess undressed. In one of their earlier conversations, she had told him that she was Scottish and he could see that the gene trait of red hair was upon her also. He liked the thought that she might be a descendent from the same clans of people as his ancestors. Maybe they were reincarnated from a time past.

All artwork was put on hold as they embraced, kissed, and played around on the soft sheets of her bed. The sun had set when Frank told her that he had a meeting in the morning and that he must get back to the base.

CHAPTER 10

The Funeral

As the sun came up the next morning, Frank was sitting outside the hut on the brim of the earthen air-raid shelter dugout. He had not slept well and had listened to the snores of twenty-three other men until he could take it no longer. The off-base visit to see Ashly had not cleared his mind of the death of Lieutenant Butt and the screams still echoed inside his head. He was sure Ashly had not enjoyed his visit the same as before. God, how he missed his friend and wished he could have done something, anything, to save the man. His feeling of guilt would not leave him. He was trained to take care of situations to save a life and had failed to do so. The lieutenant had been a great guy, a good officer and a true friend. He had been different from the other officers. He didn't make the men feel as if he were better than they were.

Frank had said he would not miss anyone; well, he was wrong, and it ached in his chest. How wrong did you have to be? The other men who had been lost from his hut were one thing, but this was something else. He had tried to compensate by seeing Ashly, and it had helped for a while, but only as long as he remained with her. This was not going away quickly.

The crew began to rouse and Alex came from the hut heading to the latrine. "What'n hell you doing sitting out here?" Alex asked.

"I'm constipated."

"Bullshit! You're just getting in aren't you? You look like shit. Been off base all night, I'll bet."

"Go piss up a rope."

"Okay, Frank, what's the matter?"

"Hell, man, I'm sorry. I'm just upset, you know, the funeral and all that stuff."

"It's okay, Frank, I feel about the same. It hurts like hell."

"I think I'll go take a shower. Wanna go along?"

"Yeah, I'll grab some towels. Be just a minute, okay?"

The entire hut was awake and moving about as Frank and Alex headed for the shower room up the road from their hut. As they walked along the road, a jeep came speeding past them and Frank recognized the officer driving.

"I thought you looked like hell, but Swartz looks like a zombie," Alex said. "Wonder what's his problem?"

Frank made no comment and just kept walking and thinking.

The cold shower jerked both men wide-awake and they began to feel more civil toward the world. After breakfast, the crew was dressing when the CQ came to the hut with a message that the truck would be there to pick them up in thirty minutes. The men rushed to dress in their best Class "A" uniforms and spit-polished shoes.

The cemetery was on the outskirts of Cambridge with a field adjacent to the entrance. The men unloaded from the trucks and walked across the field toward an assembling group of airmen. A major was directing the officers into one group and the enlisted men into another. A military band started playing a funeral march and two-by-two the men marched around the field and through the cemetery gate. The Cambridge cemetery was a beautiful place with lush green grass and shading oak trees. Many airmen had recently been laid to rest there. The odor of freshly dug earth struck Frank's nose as he stopped marching.

A small white wooden slab marked each grave, but no names were on the upright markers, only a number. That was what you became—just a number. What a lousy way to be remembered. No more having fun with your buddies; no piece of toilet paper stuck where you cut yourself shaving; no slap on the back to greet you when you least expected it; no singing over the intercom; no smiles; no laughter when you made an ass of yourself; no voice to say, "That's okay, buddy."

No nothing. Just a number.

There were so many freshly covered graves without any green grass yet covering them, and so many markers lining the grassy rolling hillside. So many buddies laid to rest here, with more added every week. The azure sky met the green in every direction, the blue, green and white contrasting with the uniforms of olive drab as 200 men got their first look at the fresh mounds of dirt. Beside each mound was a flag-draped coffin; beside each coffin stood an Honor Guard.

This day there were twenty coffins lined side-by-side in a row. Twenty men who just days ago were alive, laughing, talking, fighting, ready to give their life for their country—and they did.

In the center just beyond the row of flagged coffins

sat a small wooden platform—a dais for the Army chaplains of all faiths. Here they all came together, with no differences now. The 200 airmen stood at rigid attention with the row of fallen comrades between them and the dais. This would be their last chance to see their buddies—a last chance to say *goodbye*. Each chaplain took part in the service. As the name, rank and serial number of each fallen comrade was called out as an officer stepped to the corresponding coffin and saluted. In unison, 200 men saluted each dead hero as one-by-one each man was honored. The military band played quietly behind the rows of men as the service proceeded to a conclusion.

The airmen had been at rigid attention for forty-five minutes when a missing-man formation of B-17s made a low fly-over and the band stopped playing. Behind the airmen, a bugler played *taps* and a distant bugle resounded, the notes drifting among the white markers and fading to the horizon through the trees.

Then all was quiet and the stillness of death tore at the hearts of the living.

Gone.

The flutter of wings was heard as dozens of pigeons were flushed and circled above the flag-draped caskets.

Gone.

The military band played softly.

Gone.

Not one man wanted to move from his tracks.

Gone.

Standing at attention, they gave one final salute for all twenty men and the chaplains moved away and came among the soldiers. Not one man broke ranks, but some fell to their knees in tears. Here was not the place to be afraid to show one's feelings. This was forever.

Through his tears, Frank looked out through the white markers. He swallowed hard as his chest heaved under his blouse. Alex reached to put his hand on Frank's arm as both shed tears. God, how he hurt inside. Tears rolled down the cheeks of strong young men. Freely they flowed. Their buddies were gone—someone's husband, someone's son, someone's father, someone's lover.

Gone.

Which ones would be here next week? Some would come as observers and others would be covered by a flag—new bodies known only by a number. Which ones would not make it back here to rest?

The crowd of men—they were men now, tempered by fate of each man's loss—slowly walked away through the gate. Every man carried with him a memory that would last a lifetime. The trucks were waiting for the them. Frank's crew wanted to return to Great Ashfield, all except Frank, who was not ready just to lie around and mourn. The sadness he felt was an aching he'd neverhad to deal with before. He tried to think back now. Had there been a gun squad? Was that what had flushed the birds? How could he forget so quickly? Were there other things he had missed? Frank told the others he was going into Cambridge, as he wanted to look around the town.

In a pub, Frank met a buddy he had not seen since mechanic school back in Gulfport, Mississippi, and the two had a good time bringing each other up to date on the past year. After a beer and two hours of conversation, they parted with a handshake. Just one beer. Frank had enjoyed seeing his old buddy, Lavinski, who was now a

B-17 airplane mechanic.

Outside the pub, something strange happened, although what, Frank could not remember. There was only a blank spot where a memory should have been as he opened his eyes and looked around. Where the hell was he? He sat up and saw that he was in a hotel room— but where? And how the hell did he get here? What happened?

He was fully dressed and the bed did not appear as if anyone had slept there. His cap was neatly folded and placed under his left epaulet. He stood up and checked his pockets, finding his off-base pass and all his money. Everything seemed to be in order, but where was he? Was he still in Cambridge? Had to be! He did not remember ever seeing a hotel in Cambridge, though. Damn, one beer was not enough to make him go blind drunk—no way; yet, he could not remember how he had gotten here, wherever here was.

Feeling sheepish, he walked downstairs and through the lobby, past the desk clerk and outside. He turned and looked back at the hotel. He knew this place. It was a hotel in London located not far from the Red Cross Club! He had never been inside this hotel, but had walked past it going to the club.

He was sixty miles from Cambridge! What in hell had happened to him? How did he get here? He tried to remember his actions, but had no memory after leaving his friend at the pub in Cambridge. He had left the cemetery and gone into town where he met his buddy, Lavinski, and they had drunk a beer—one beer—and talked. Then they parted and he walked down the street— but to where? Nothing! That was the last he could remember until waking up here in London.

Frank checked his pockets and again counted his money. How had he traveled to London and it had not cost a shilling? The hotel clerk had not said anything when he walked out, so the room must have been paid for. What in the hell had he done? What had happened to him?

He thought about the funeral and all the fresh graves. He remembered the ceremony and how he had cried for his friend. His heart had been wrenched in his chest. God, he missed Lieutenant Butt. The pain his friend had suffered made Frank's mind quiver. He should have been able to do something to save his life. Even now, he could hear the screams in his head; now his buddy was only a number among all the other numbers. Those last words he had spoken were burnt into Frank's memory: "Give 'em hell boys . . . I'm done for."

Was his reaction to all these events enough to blow his mind? It must have been the funeral. There was no other explanation, but still, that did not explain what had happened to him. None of it was good enough. Was he ready for a Section-8 discharge for a mental condition?

Frank must have stood there for an hour before he looked at his watch. The time was 4:00 p.m., but what day was it? It couldn't still be the day of the funeral—could it? No, that had to have been yesterday or some other day. What should he do? Then he looked at his pass from the base and saw it was good for two days. Damn, he had to check the date somehow. He did not want to be AWOL. His first thought was to catch a train and return to base.

"Guess I'd better get my ass to Paddington Station

and check the train schedule," he thought.

Frank took a taxi to Paddington Station, wondering how to find out what day it was. He could ask the driver, of course, but how would he do it and not sound like a nut? He really felt like a nut. He finally asked, and the driver told him it was July 11. He looked at Frank oddly as Frank paid his fare. A whole day gone from his life—over 24 hours, and he had nothing to show for it. What happens to someone to cause this sort of effect? Had he become mentally unstable and not qualified to do his job?

Frank was completely dumbfounded. He had attended but one other funeral in his life, for his great-grandfather, who had been a Confederate soldier, wounded in battle, but he survived the war. He had died at home in 1932 when Frank was only eight years old. All the airmen buried at Cambridge were young men, twenty-six at the oldest. He could not see a parallel.

He sure didn't understand what had caused him to lose an entire day from his life. Should he go back to the base and talk it out with Alex? Or should he stay here in London and see Nichole? His pass was good for another day. Alex was ninety miles away and Nichole was just a taxi ride from here. Maybe a break from the base would be the best idea as he did not think he could stand it if the other men had been affected the same as he. Maybe Nichole could help him forget the horror of all that had taken place recently.

Nichole won the mind game!

The train would not leave for Stowmarket for another hour and he would use that time to make sure his decision was correct. He decided to walk from Paddington Station to the Club. It would give him time to think about his decision. Although he had no reason to purchase anything, he stopped along the street and looked in shop windows. He was just looking and thinking, still confused as to what had happened to him.

Frank knew he should go back and talk with Alex. Alex was his closest friend and he did not want Nichole or anyone else to know what had happened to him. "Man I'm in big trouble," he thought. "No way I'm going to let anybody know about this."

It was insane—a blackout in his mind. He would have to figure a way to deal with it. Could he build a mental tomb in his mind and put it all away? What would his crewmen or the flight surgeon say?

When Frank arrived at the Red Cross Club, he found Nichole had left for the restaurant. A taxi was the fastest means to get there and he quickly located one. He wondered if he could be with Nichole and not let her know what had happened to him. She was always so full of life and ready to have fun.

"Yeah, Nichole can help me get my mind off whatever has happened," he thought as he rode to the Greek restaurant. "We can have a ball and that should do the trick for me."

Nichole was happy to see him. Off in a side room she gave him a warm welcome and told him she wanted to leave the restaurant as soon as possible.

"Why all the rush?" he asked.

"I'll tell you later. Let's get out of here."

"Want to take a taxi?"

"Yes, that would be best."

"Com'on, I'll bet I have one ready to go."

"You didn't have a cabby wait did you?"

"No, but I don't think he's busy and I tipped him good."

The cab was waiting just as Frank had guessed and Nichole said she wanted to go to her flat. She did not talk during the ride and Frank wondered what her problem was. She seemed worried about something but he didn't have a clue as to what it might be. Was it something he did or did not do?

"Can I ask why all the rush to leave the restaurant? You always seemed so pleased there. What's wrong?"

"Something happened there and I don't want to tell you about it now. I'll tell you after I settle down. Is that all right?"

"Sure. I don't mean to pry into your business . . . just curious, that's all. I don't need to know."

"Great. Let's have ourselves a good time, then, while we can."

"Sounds good to me. Any suggestions?"

"Do you remember my comment about Apollo?"

"Hell, I couldn't forget that on my deathbed."

"Please do not use that phrase."

"Damn, you're really upset. What can I do to help?"

"Just be yourself. Like you have been before."

"That requires me taking off my clothes and you have not eaten yet. You're the one who's always hungry."

"See, you are yourself. That's the way I want you to be."

"Come here and I'll show you just how I can be."

Frank did not have a clue as to her problem. He only knew that she was acting strangely, but he didn't know what he might say or do to help or worsen the situation. He wasn't feeling so damn good himself, so why waste time? For the lack of a better idea, he took Nichole in his arms and held her tight, vowing not to speak unless necessary. What was there to say? Her warm body felt great pressed against his and he no longer thought of his problems.

She spoke first. "I am hungry. I didn't realize I've not eaten today until you reminded me just now. Yes, let's go down the street and eat. That would be nice."

"See, I knew you needed to be fed, then everything will be okay. I'm ready if you are."

Frank had not taken off his blouse and was ready, but Nichole wanted to change clothes before they went out. Maybe whatever was bothering her would be less of a problem on a full stomach. He did not understand why women wanted sex only after they had eaten. It gave him a sour stomach to eat before sex. Had to be a female thing. He did not want any alcohol either as it always worked in reverse for him. He grinned when he thought of the brothel back home and his reaction to all the homebrew and the antics of that female. Cold sober was the *only* way to have sex.

Nichole knew of a restaurant nearby. She said the food was not all that great but it was convenient and just a short walk from her flat. The dining area was in the basement of a building and was larger than any Frank had ever seen. It could probably seat 1,000 people without a problem.

They had almost finished eating when a roving string trio stopped to play at their table and he saw her face brighten.

"Is that Grecian music?" he asked.

Nichole's face glowed. "You recognize the music?

That's just wonderful. I've been here before and they remembered I enjoy the music. I came here once with Alfred and they played that same song. I'm overjoyed how the two of you are—were—so much alike. Please forgive me, I should not have said that. I'm sure you think hard of me for reminding you of him all the time."

"Not at all. I only hope someone will think as much of me when I'm gone. He had to be so very special for you."

She changed the subject quickly and started talking about the many soldiers that had once visited the club and no longer came. She assumed the men had left when the invasion started.

Nichole had a glass of wine after eating but Frank abstained. He thought about telling her why, but thought better of it and kept quiet.

The English summer night was unusually warm and there was not a breeze to be felt, as the heavy blackout drapes prevented fresh air from entering the flat. Frank was in a full sweat in the closed room and had to remove his tie and shirt because he had always produced a great amount of sweat. He imagined he would sweat a lot before this night was over and so would Nichole.

His mind went back to the funeral and his lost day and he knew Nichole was bothered by something else. He wanted both of them to think of something other than their troubles. Nichole went into the bathroom to change clothes and when she came out, she was wearing an outfit of white silk trimmed in gold. Frank had seen this type of dress in drawings in books when studying about foreign lands, but the drawings did not do justice to what he was looking at in real life.

"Have you ever seen the Grecian dance of love?"

"No, but I'm sure I would enjoy seeing you perform it."

Nichole's ancestral heritage must have included some of the Amazonian genes because for five minutes, she danced as she clapped her hands to a rhythm with her steps. Frank had seen movies of hula dancers in grass skirts, which he enjoyed, but the graceful swaying of hula hips did not stand a chance when compared to the dance by Nichole. Each step, every body movement was designed to enhance the erogenous effect on an observer. As he watched, sweat poured from his entire body. Drenched, he knew his clothing had to come off or he would surely suffocate. He rose and they stood there, with her knowing the dance had been successful in reaching her goal.

Apollo and Aphrodite stood in the middle of the floor, the myth no longer a myth. Zeus would have been pleased. The gods had returned to human form on earth. The temple of the gods thundered with approval for them as they shared their empowered talents. Their bodies were slippery with lustful moisture as they lay upon the bed wrestling, as if for their very lives. Finally, they rested.

Frank heard the clock strike two as Nichole rose and pulled open the heavy blackout drapes. The midsummer night air had cooled and a fresh breeze whiffed through the room as they sat on the bed in absolute blackness while the city of London slept. The nightly German air raids had not happened so far tonight—perhaps the Germans were busy bombing some other city.

"Are you ready to hear why I was upset earlier?" she

asked.

"Only if you really want to tell me."

"I think you should know. I would rather tell you than for it to come to you by surprise."

"If you think I need to know, then go ahead and tell me."

"It has to do with my sister. I had not mentioned her to you before since there was no need. She lived here in London until last fall and that was the reason for a discussion at the restaurant yesterday. Our parents are reasonably wealthy, as well as our relatives here in London. It may have been boredom or who knows what, but she started a life that upset us. She was not satisfied dating some nice man and wanted more men to bed her. Then she discovered it could be profitable, so she became one of the street girls, which I think you Americans call Piccadilly Commandos. It was not long before she met this American officer and he helped her acquire more lucrative clientele here in London. She lived in a six-room suite in a hotel with a décor to behold. The lieutenant was taking money for arranging all the so-called dates. First it was all military men, then she became known to the wealthy Lords in London, and the Lords quickly decided they wanted her all for themselves. This did not satisfy her lust and the lieutenant talked her into moving someplace north of here, to some sort of high-class brothel with many military officers as clients. The officers did not stay around long, therefore she had many new lovers and that seemed to satisfy her lust. She liked living in the country away from all the bombing here in London. I know little more other than she became wealthy on her own. Much money poured into her bank account but she did not know how to handle it and let the lieutenant be her banker."

Nichole stopped talking and looked at Frank as if to see what he thought of her story. Seeing that he was listening intensely, she continued.

"This past week she showed up at the restaurant needing money. It seems the officer had somehow emptied her bank account and not only that, she was pregnant. So there, you have the entire story and you can see that I'm not as nice a person for having told you. I thought you might understand, so now what do you think of me? If you choose to go I will understand."

Frank had many thoughts running through his mind but could not see where all this had any bearing on his and Nichole's relationship.

"I think I understand your emotions and how you may think I would react toward you. But this has nothing to do with you and me. You're different from her and that I know for sure. Yes, you were lonely when we first met and I was as much to blame as you were on that first date. Your beauty has bewitched me and I'm still the same person just as you are the same sweet girl I first met. If it were not for my job of flying and the probable death that will come, I might think different about us. Anything else is out of the question, as we first agreed. If that is off your mind and I'm aware of the situation, let's just put it behind us. I'll help you if I can, so maybe we should start from here and go on with our lives?"

Nichole sat with her head in her hands, staring at the floor. It took several minutes for all she and Frank had said to settle in her mind and offset her concerns. Finally, she looked up and smiled.

"Yes, you are correct and we can put it behind us and go on as we were. So, no more about my sister. She can work out her own problems. I wish things were different and we could be together always. I really love you, Frank."

Nichole turned up the volume on the radio and they lay back on the bed enjoying the fresh night air. Sweat had dampened the sheet but Frank couldn't have cared less. He had other thoughts on his mind. Could it have any connection? She had said it was an American officer—a lieutenant—north of London—a brothel—the officer wanting money. He remembered looking through the peephole and seeing Swartz and the woman in bed. And there were the arrangements made by Swartz for him to meet Ashly. Was there a connection? No, it was too far fetched and he was grasping at straws. Many American officers would fit all that information.

Frank had heard that many American soldiers were sending bundles of cash back to the States, but he never concerned himself with where they got their hands on so much money. He was either too dumb to get in on the act or he just didn't have that much need for money. He would probably never live to enjoy money sent to the States anyway.

He looked at Nichole and wondered what was on her mind. Was she thinking of her sister being pregnant? What about their Nichole? Frank had often neglected to use protection. If she were so upset about her sister's situation, perhaps he should broach the subject. No way did he want the responsibility of a child as he flew more combat missions. He had heard of soldiers being taken in by women so they could get their benefits.

Nichole turned her head and was looking at him. It must have been something in his face—or else, she was psychic.

"You should not be concerned about me, Frank. My aunt here in London helped me through my move to womanhood and taught me to know my body. I'm aware of what we're doing, so do not be surprised if one day I tell you to wait."

"Damn, you're psychic. I'm glad you're my friend. You really did read my mind just now."

She laughed and said, "I know what you have on your mind and I love you for it."

In the low light of a candle he looked and saw the beauty of this woman. The naked human body had to be the most beautiful creation of all God's work.

The next day, with Nichole as tour guide, Frank looked at the ruined sections of London. She wanted him to see the destruction caused by the years of bombing. The air raids were nightly now and when Frank was in London, he heard the bombs exploding. He had been lucky on his trips here and no bombs had fallen close to him.

As they passed a hotel, Nichole asked the cabby to stop, and with Frank in tow, she walked to the entrance of the hotel where her sister had once owned the apartment or suite. Seeing the grandeur of the lobby, Frank thought it must have cost a bundle to live there. The dress and manners of the men he saw in the lobby indicated money, big bucks. He did not see any women.

"Do you see what style my sister lived in?" she asked.

"I would think it hard to give up," he replied.

Leaving the hotel, they went to the Greek restaurant

for lunch. He wondered how this place could survive with so few diners and asked Nichole how they could manage to stay open.

"My relatives have connections here where they control all the first class food distributed throughout the London area. I believe you would call it *black market*. The restaurant is necessary for maintaining the connection. They had to start this operation or else they would have had to close the doors long ago. See, I am not from as nice a family after all."

"Nichole, I know I asked for it, but the less I know the better, in the event some asshole drags me in for questioning."

His thoughts were really on Swartz and Nichole's sister. The man could be capable of most anything, including having him killed or at least busted in rank and put in the stockade. Who knew what Swartz was into?

After their good-byes, Frank left for Paddington Station and boarded the train for Great Ashfield.

CHAPTER 11

Return to War

During the 90-mile ride back to Great Ashfield, Frank thought about the death of Lieutenant Butt, about his lost day and about what Nichole had said concerning her sister. If there was a connection between Nichole's sister and Swartz, he wanted to find out. If Swartz played the game as Frank thought he did, then he questioned whether Ashly could be a victim? He had been confused about why Aunt Amy had looked into his background. He thought it strange, as if he were being selected for a particular reason. He would have to follow up on that as well. Where should he start? Perhaps with Swartz himself, he decided.

"Missed you being around last night," Alex said when Frank got back to the hut. "Guess you went to London again, huh? How was Nichole?"

"Had to try and get my mind off the funeral. Guess I should've come back here. You okay?"

"Yeah, I'm okay, Frank. Hope Nichole was able to help."

"It worked for a while," Frank said.

"The Horse has been repaired and is ready to go. Guess we'd better look at the list for our names," Alex replied.

They discovered that the loading list had the crew of the Horse scheduled for another mission.

As Frank walked from the hut at 4:00 a.m., the night air cut a chill over his body. A boyish grin came to his face as he considered how much warmer he'd been the night before. He thought, "Damn, an Army bunk! But not so fast Frank. This war has brought you from a country boy to a worldly man, knowing two beautiful women. Yet, will you live long enough to enjoy them?" He considered the probability of his surviving all the missions was slim to none. At the hardstand, he looked at the Horse sitting there so quietly, its olive drab color a reflection of his feelings.

No doubt, the roar of the engines on the 35 heavy bombers awakened surrounding villagers, although they had probably become accustomed to this noise during these past months. Frank wondered if the people could tell by the sound that there were sometimes not as many coming back as had gone out. The people had few ways of showing appreciation for the efforts of the American airmen other than by placing fresh flowers in the mess halls.

The dark early morning sky was filled with airplane identification lights as the bombers climbed into the dark skies. There were more than usual this day as three heavy bomber groups circled upward to form a wing of 105 airplanes, all heading toward the same target. They were going to the German city of Munich, a city in a sense similar to London—a congested area of German people who had been spared the ravages of war, until now. But all that would end in a few hours. Tranquillity would be a thing of the past, nothing but a memory for the people in Munich.

The bombers were each loaded with twelve 500-

pound incendiary bombs and they were under orders to *burn the city*. Herr Hitler had to be shown what bombing London was like, so this mission was pure revenge. God help the people below when the rain of fire fell upon them. Their lives would change this day, a day many people would never forget.

The huge air armada circled and gathered into a formation over England, then headed east for the target. Condensation trails advertised the route of bombers as the huge armada flew into German air space. The cold dry air ate through the fur-lined flight suits and chilled the airmen's bones. Frank shivered and took a deep breath of oxygen as he jotted in his notes: July 13, 1944, Mission number 16, D-Day + 37. Target: Munich, Germany. Long flight, estimated 9 hours in the sky. Expect heavy defense from the Germans. Good luck!

Damn, how he missed the hot sultry night when sweat had poured from his body as he lay there in London. He would never complain about the heat again. He had been told that hell was a raging furnace, but he knew otherwise; it had to have been frozen over. If he lived to make it back to the States, he should consider moving to Florida or some other hot climate. He shivered again at the thoughts.

Frank had lost his breakfast again this morning, which was becoming a habit and he did not like it. He had to grin when he considered that maybe there had been a backfire and he was the pregnant one. Hell, it would be worth it after all the pleasures he was having. Then he stopped grinning! Could Nichole or Ashly be pregnant? Oh shit! Had Ashly lied to him? He had never before had an experience like he did that first time with her. It had been so sudden, so intense, so everything. Why had it felt so different? He sure didn't want some female having his baby and using that as a reason to get to the States, as he had heard some of the soldiers had been trapped into doing.

The early morning light revealed the coastline of the Netherlands below. People were still sleeping down there. If they only knew the power of destruction flying over their heads.

"Get your mind back on your business or your worries will be over," he thought. "Someone down there is awake."

Flak began to pop into the formation and a B-17 with an engine on fire dropped from the formation and turned to head back to base. Then another B-17 suddenly exploded in a ball of white-hot fire as it received a direct hit in the bomb bay and all twelve incendiaries exploded at once. The flak stopped as the formation flew out of range of the anti-aircraft guns.

"Three hours since we left home and here comes company," Frank thought as German fighters came into his view.

"Bandits at six o'clock low!" he shouted over the intercom.

The German fighters had been approaching from the rear using the condensation trails left by the bombers as cover. The pilot alerted the formation commander and all gunners were ready. Koop and Frank opened fire at the same time as two ME-109s dropped below their airplane and flew into full view of Frank's sights. At a distance of 500 yards, he saw his tracer bullets hitting one of the fighters. He continued to fire ten-round bursts from his guns until he saw pieces coming off the fighter and falling away. Then the ME-109 spiraled to the ground.

The thought in Frank's mind was, "That's for Lieutenant Butt, you sorry son of a bitch. How do you like them apples?"

He then switched to another fighter and caught him going away. As he fired, smoke began trailing from the airplane and it headed for the earth.

Frank felt the jarring of the Horse as the gunners above him fired at fighters he could not see. A B-17 fell from formation and headed earthward in a spiraling dive. He saw two more fighters go down and then they quit attacking and flew away. Frank watched the German fighters head away to the north until they were out of sight. He had made sure they were not returning for another attack. They had a good reason to leave because the anti-aircraft batteries around Munich started firing, the bursts of flak beginning to form a huge black cloud, lighting the sky with red flashes of shells bursting.

Frank turned his turret and looked at the Horse's wingman. At that instant, a shell hit that B-17 in the bomb bay and it became just one big white ball of fire as all the incendiary bombs exploded. Only the four engines fell away from the now red-hot cloud that was once an airplane. Ten men vaporized in a puff.

Frank spun his turret away from the sight.

The bombs were dropped and Frank watched them fall away from the open bomb bay. As they reached a preset altitude, each bomb broke into fifty 10-pound sticks of white-hot burning fire. Through the black smoke from the bursting shells, he could see them strewn over the city of Munich. In minutes, the city became a firestorm from the 60,000 burning sticks of fire.

As the formation reached the Rally Point, Frank could see two B-17s straggling behind and below the Horse. While he watched, three ME-109s came into view, out of his gun range, and made quick work of shooting down the straggling bombers. Gone. Twenty more men lost in seconds.

Frank's only consolation was that he could see the city of Munich in flames, and smoke from the burning city reached the 10,000-foot level in only minutes. The fighters had left, so he sat and watched the city burn. Fortunately, the flak had stopped popping around the formation.

As he watched, he thought, "Well, Herr Hitler, let's see how you respond to this weenie roast." Then he thought, "Damn, I wonder if any of my counterparts were down there with their ladies? Holy crap, what a lousy thought. Gott im Himmel!"

The return home was about the same as going in except there were no more German fighters. Over the Channel, the formation broke up into three groups and headed for their bases. Frank could tell that many B-17s were missing as he noticed holes, where there should have been airplanes, in the two formations of bombers.

The ambulances were busy when the Horse finally landed at Great Ashfield. Many airmen had been wounded today and Frank did not want to think of how many had been killed and lost over Germany. The Air Corps had paid dearly this day.

At the mess hall, the Officer in Charge of the grog slipped Frank an extra shot of Scotch. He had lost his breakfast and now found he still was not hungry. This agony of men dying around them and getting their asses shot off was getting to everyone on the crew. Frank could sense it in every word they spoke. No one wanted to admit that they were losing it, but it was obvious. On a mission, no one said a word that was not necessary. Now Frank knew why so many asked for ground jobs. It would not have surprised him if someone on his crew asked for relief, but Frank had resigned himself to an early death and was just trying to make the best of it until his time came. He hoped that when it happened, it came fast, and not like Lieutenant Butt.

As Frank walked to the shower, he met Lieutenant Swartz on the road. His first impulse was to clobber the bastard, but he thought better of it and spoke to the lieutenant.

"How's it going over at Dame Metcalf's?" asked Frank. The words were not out of his mouth before he realized he had said the wrong thing.

"Between you and me, it has gone to hell."

"Sorry I asked. Thought things may have changed for you."

"They've changed all right—for the worst."

"Well, it can't be any worse than these missions."

"Frank, you just don't know. I may have to go on one and maybe I'll get lucky and get shot down. I could take a rest and sit out the balance of the war in a German Gulag."

"Things can't be that bad."

"What you don't know, Frank, is that I wish I was dead."

"Want to talk about it?"

"You don't want to know. Besides, I gotta go. See you around, maybe. By the way, Ashly said she'd like to see you. Take care, tally-ho."

Swartz went his way and Frank thought, "How about that. Sounds like he's got his ass in a sling. Guess I'd better go check on Ashly and see what's going on over there."

After showering and dressing, Frank, as tired as he was, pedaled his bike to the mansion. He had to see if Ashly was all right. The conversation with Swartz had tweaked his curiosity. Frank wondered why Swartz was so down. Open talk about death was not common. Were some of the pieces of this puzzle starting to fit? Why did Ashly want to see him? Maybe she really missed him, as he did her.

It was about 6:00 p.m. when Frank arrived at the mansion. The butler let him in and then went for Ashly. As he waited, Frank looked around the room and considered just how much money this place must be worth.

"Oh Frank, I'm so glad you came," Ashly said, rushing to greet him. "I've been so worried about you. I learned of the death of your navigator from Lieutenant Swartz and it sounded so terrible. I'm so sorry for you and wondered how you were taking the death." Tears came to her eyes and she grabbed and hugged him before he could speak.

"I'm okay—just had to let it sink in that Lieutenant Butt was really gone. I realize it's late, but can I stay for a while?"

"You can stay as long as you please, silly boy. Come with me to my room where we will be alone."

As they climbed the stairs, Frank noticed no one else was around and thought Aunt Amy must be with her card buddies. There were a number of vehicles parked outside.

In Ashly's room, she hugged him as never before, then pulled back a covering from the portrait and said, "Look at my American country boy now. I think he looks stunning and I love to look upon him."

She must have worked on the painting for many hours, as it seemed more than half-finished. Frank could tell that she was a fine portrait painter as he stared at himself on the canvas, his nude body looking as if he were standing in front of a mirror.

"I see you've come to your senses," he said.

"And just what do you mean by that remark? Oh, I know what you're looking at first. What do you think?"

"Looks normal to me," he said and laughed out loud.

"I have missed that laugh so much. You are a joy."

"Ashly, before I say more about the painting, I'd like to ask a few questions—not about us, about someone else."

"Anything you want to know will be fine, if I have the answer. I do not mind at all."

"I saw Lieutenant Swartz and he seemed out of sorts. Talked most unlike what I expected. Do you have any clue as to why that may be? He talked like there might be a problem here."

"That is a real story. I have overheard conversations when I probably should not have listened, but I did. He has a problem with one of the women. He also owes Aunt Amy a great deal of money. He has lived here for the past few weeks, with the same woman. I'm sure she is pregnant with his child. She went away for a few days but has returned. That woman knew how to take care of herself but failed to do so. One day I stepped in the room that I showed you and looked at the gamblers and watched how they handled money as if it were nothing. There were many British and American officers playing at the tables. Before I left the room I sneaked a peek in one of the bedrooms and there was Lieutenant Swartz arguing with that woman. That was most unusual, as they both were very angry. That's when I learned what I just told you."

"Yeah, that could be part of the problem, but money also seems to be in there somewhere. Sounds like he may be losing his butt gambling. Or he has a rat hole taking all his cash. Who knows what the man is into with all I hear he's doing? I sure wouldn't want to be in his shoes. These women that live here, are they locals? Do you know any of their names?"

"I know the last name of the woman living with Lieutenant Swartz. Her name is Karros."

"Holy shit!" thought Frank. "What a small world this is."

"What's the matter? Did I say something wrong? You appear as if you just saw a ghost, Frank."

"It may be nothing more than my not having eaten much lately," he said, realizing it was a half-truth. "I lost my breakfast again this morning. Must have been something I ate that did not suit my stomach—or else I'm pregnant also."

She smiled and said, "You silly boy, you are very funny. I'm the one who should worry about that." A tear came to her eyes as she turned away.

Frank imagined he could kiss his money goodbye.

That Swartz must be in crap up to his neck. What was he going to do about the pregnant woman? Would they rid her of the child or was she planning on going back to the States with Swartz? Frank believed Swartz was a married man, at least for the present. But all that was not his concern as long as he stayed clear and did not cross Swartz. He would stay clear, and that was a promise. The man was a walking time bomb and anyone in his way would likely pay a price with his head.

Frank walked from the painting to where Ashly was now standing and they looked each other in the eyes.

"Have I done something wrong?" she asked.

"Yes," he answered, "you have not asked me to remove my clothing since I've been here—not once."

Without saying a word, Ashly smiled and started loosening his necktie and unbuttoning his shirt. Frank liked the idea that someone thought enough of him to share their feelings with him, and he no longer had any hang-ups about being naked before her. For him, this seemed the correct way to live in this world now.

The sensation of the caressing summer breeze over their naked bodies, the moonlight and the kisses, drugged them with passion. Frank had begun to sweat and a drop fell from the tip of his nose and landed on Ashly's forehead. As he kissed it away, they floated to a world of pure ecstasy. The full moon shown through the open French doors, lighting the half-painted portrait. When Frank turned his head and looked, it was as if someone were standing there in the shadows with moonlight revealing their hiding place. He thought of the ghost and wondered if Richard was watching over this place.

Later he saw that Ashly was enjoying peaceful bliss

as she slept and his mind reeled with the pleasure of knowing that this girl, his Princess, had just days ago been a virgin. Now they shared the pangs of joy that brought them both into this world. She had selected him over many others of her elite, brash and arrogant male friends to share the pleasure of a new life. He could not understand why. Was there more to this union than he knew? Why had Dame Metcalf researched his background?

Damned war! Would he live long enough to share a life already consummated? He had seen Ashly hide her tears when he arrived. What had been on her mind? Did she really fear for his life? She was so beautiful lying there. Yes, he loved the sight of his Princess. She was magnificent.

Frank noticed she was relaxed as she slept. He kissed her forehead and arose from the bed. With a pencil from her table, he jotted a note for her to find when she awoke. He then pinned the paper to the frame of the half-finished portrait and quiet-like-a-mouse, he dressed and left the room. He went down the stairs and to the rear entry door where the butler sat nodding. With a tip of his cap to Charles, Frank departed into the night.

CHAPTER 12

The Rest Home

In his note, Frank had told Ashly that he had left the base without a pass and that he must return because his name might be on the list to fly. He hated to leave her but had no choice and hoped she understood. The moon lighted the lane to the base as he rode his bike—the same moon that had washed over the bed and delighted his eyes at the sight of his Princess as she slept.

The 10:30 list of names on the bulletin board did not include the crew of the Horse. Damn! He had to sleep on that rough Army blanket instead of the soft sheets he had just left. He lay there thinking of Ashly, and her willingness to try and make his life more enjoyable. Finally, he slept.

"Out again all night, Frank? We've been discussing whether we should make a little extra money by renting out your bunk," Alex teased as they washed their faces the next morning.

"Make the arrangements with HQ and I'll go on permanent pass. You'll be welcome to the cash."

"The First Sergeant said we were to report to squadron HQ after breakfast."

"Guess I've stepped in somebody's shit again," Frank said. "But why everybody's?" He wondered why he felt paranoid whenever something happened.

"Don't know. Just told you what he said."

The First Sergeant met with the crew and told them they had been ordered to a retreat for a few days, starting today. He added that the bus would be at squadron HQ in one hour, and for them to pack their bags and be ready to leave.

The hour passed quickly as the crew made ready. Frank thought he and the others should have seemed happier than they appeared. The long ride on the bus was bumpy and no one had any idea where they were heading. The bright morning sun indicated they were headed west. The men were silent with their own thoughts during the three-hour ride. Frank was disappointed he had not been able to let Ashly know he would be gone for this period. He knew she would be worried unless Swartz let her know. Since he had no control, the situation would just have to work itself out.

The long paved driveway through the overhanging trees led the bus to a large country manor. As Frank scanned the estate, he thought this place must belong to some wealthy Englishman. Some people that Frank recognized as Red Cross workers were waiting for them to offload, including an Army nurse and an officer who had the appearance of a doctor.

After some pleasant greetings, the crewmen were shown to upstairs bedrooms, with real beds, sheets and pillows. Then they were escorted downstairs to the parlor where they met the doctor and the nurse assisting him. The doctor stated that each man would receive a complete physical examination starting immediately after this meeting. The ones not being examined were free to look around and the Red Cross workers would be their guides.

Koop's name was first on the list and he was asked

to stay with the doctor while the other five men left with aides to tour the house and grounds. It was a large place with well-manicured grounds. There were flowers planted everywhere and a gardener was tending the huge lawn. This seemed so far away from war that it was hard to imagine fighting was going on so near. This place, which had a full domestic staff complete with upstairs maids, had been taken over by the Army Air Corps and used to give airmen a break from their missions.

The balance of the first day and the entire next day were spent in the examination of the men. No one seemed in a hurry and no orders were given, which suited the men. Had it had not been for the good food and beds, it would have been boring, but the staff was most accommodating.

Alex and Frank soon became bored and decided to put to use some bicycles they found. While riding on a country lane, they came upon a group of British women working in the fields. Nothing would do but for Alex to stop and watch the women, who appeared to be healthy young girls, dressed in men's white shirts and bright orange overalls. Lighted by the sun, the workers stood out in the fields as they worked.

As Frank and Alex stood in the shade of a tree and watched, the women took a water break, and this was when Frank noticed the covered water buckets near where he and Alex stood. The group of women came to the tree and drank, then rested in the shade. Alex was delighted when two of the girls engaged him in conversation. Frank listened as they told of being drafted into the British Women's Farming Corps. Their job was to help feed the nation while the men served in the military. The women said they worked long and hard hours planting and saving the crops, moving as needed from farm to farm.

It did not take long for the women to talk Alex into making a date for him and Frank after supper. They were to meet under this tree at around 8:00 p.m. Frank could see the girls' tent encampment about a quarter mile away in a grove of trees.

After dinner, coffee was served in the drawing room and all the men sat around and chewed the fat with the aides. A few minutes later, Alex and Frank excused themselves, slipped away from the others and rode the bikes to their prearranged meeting. Upon arrival, they sat under the tree smoking as they waited for the girls to arrive. As darkness came and no one showed up, they laughed, thinking they had been stood up. Frank did not much care, as his thoughts were of Ashly and his having to leave on such short notice. He would much rather have been with her.

Suddenly, a loud whisper fell on Frank's ear. He looked toward where the sound originated and there were the two girls crouched low beside the hedgerow some fifty feet away. They quickly came toward the two airmen.

Frank had thought it might be fun to sit and talk with the girls but the reason for this meeting became clear in a flash as one of the girls grabbed Alex and began smothering him with kisses. The other one with the blond hair took Frank by the hand and pulled him away. He did not like her being so aggressive, as one of his quirks was not to have a female act so pushy. It was just not his cup of tea. But this blond was strongly built, muscular from all the farm work, and had no problem pulling him with her.

"Let's walk into the woods," she insisted as she pulled him along. Before he realized just how expert she could be in removing them, her orange overalls were lying on the ground and he was astounded by her lack of reservation and obvious desire for him.

From a short distance away came a tinkling sound as Alex's GI belt buckle jingled.

"What's that noise?" asked the blond.

"That's just Alex getting his ashes hauled," he told her.

It was near midnight when the blond named Carrie told Frank they had bed check at midnight and had better be getting back to their tent.

"Can you bring some of your friends tomorrow night?" she asked. "We'll meet here at the same time."

Frank thought, "Yeah, but I won't be one of them."

Alex told the girls that he and some others would meet them tomorrow evening, same time as tonight.

The next morning after breakfast Frank was called to the doctor for his examination. First, the doctor asked him several questions about his combat missions. He told the doctor he had been uptight at times, such as after the funeral, but he did not let the doctor know about the lost day from his life. He said it really bothered him when some of his buddies were lost and others killed. Then he said, "I've found a way to relieve some of the pain. I've met some really nice girls—one in particular."

The doctor said, "Nothing wrong with that as long as you're careful. Always take care of yourself."

Then came the physical examination—the check for

hernias: turn your head and cough; strip it down; bend over and spread 'em. Then the finger. The whole nine yards.

Upon completion of his examination, the doctor said, "You're a healthy young buck."

"Haven't been sick very often, so far."

"It's rare to find a young man who's gone through what you have and is still in such good shape."

"It sure can't be the Army food."

"Your prostate and other plumbing is healthy. Try keeping it that way. Exercise is good for all your body parts. I can tell you've had your clock cleaned lately. Wasn't one of the aides, was it? We need them and don't want them getting pregnant."

"No sir! I wouldn't think of doing something like that."

"Okay, Mays, you've got a clean bill of health."

Frank had not removed his shoes and the doctor did not see the deep bruise on his heel. He was glad, afraid the doctor would ground him from flying if he'd seen it.

Late that morning while playing volleyball, King fell into Frank's right leg and his knee popped so loudly that everyone thought it was broken. They carried him back to the doctor for an examination of his leg, where he discovered his knee was badly sprained, but fortunately not broken. The doctor taped Frank from his thigh down to his ankle so his leg could not bend and told him to go to the flight surgeon upon return to base. Frank spent the balance of the day having people care for him. The knee hurt like hell but he really enjoyed all the care and attention.

When night came he was in no shape to keep the date

with the girls and was sort of glad he didn't have to go. He turned Carrie over to Mark and told him to have a good time. Alex, Mark and King went to the rendezvous.

After dinner, Frank went to bed, but when the three returned late that night they woke him, telling what a good time they had. Frank had been dreaming of Ashly, his Princess, and her castle.

The bus came for the men the next day and they returned to Great Ashfield, where the first news they heard was that another crew from the hut had been shot down over Germany while they were gone. Frank was beside himself. "Damn, damn! This is some welcome back," he yelled. "How many more from this hut? It must be cursed."

Frank was not about to go to the base doctor with his injured knee because he feared he would be grounded. Instead, he cut the tape with his pocketknife so it would bend some. He walked with a noticeable limp and it hurt like hell.

Sleep did not come easy that first night back at base, and when Frank did fall asleep, he again experienced his awful nightmares.

CHAPTER 13

Back to Combat

So much for rest homes. "Big Deal!" thought Frank. That night the crew of the Horse found their names on the loading list for a mission the next morning. It hurt to think of the airmen who were missing, and no one wanted to talk to the new crew that moved in the day Frank's crew went to the rest home.

Frank wondered how many men had slept in this hut? And how many rested in the cemetery at Cambridge? How many were shot down and scattered over the fields of Germany? Maybe some were prisoners in Gulags. It was not a pretty picture, nor a good selection of questions to think about when trying to go to sleep, but the training finally worked its charm and Frank drifted off into his private land of nightmares.

The next morning at the Horse, everything seemed back to normal. The airplane and equipment were checked and double-checked. The propellers had been *walked through* to clear the cylinders of latent oil and built up gas. The Horse was ready to go and the men wandered around wasting time, waiting for the signal to take off.

Frank walked over and talked with friends at the airplane parked next to the Horse. After a few minutes, the pilot of that plane called for an all clear, as he wanted to test run one of the engines. With it up and running, he revved it wide open several times. The noise overpowered conversations and the men stopped talking. Then one of the men stood and said something that no one understood. He then turned and walked toward the airplane, and as they watched, he put his arm up as if to wave goodbye. He then turned and walked directly into the rotating propeller.

GOD! What a sight! Why? Why? What made him do that?

The pilot immediately cut the engine and the co-pilot radioed for medics. As the other men waited for the propeller to stop rotating, Frank walked back toward the Horse. When away from the airplane, he stopped and threw up. Alex had looked when someone yelled, and as Frank came to him with tears in his eyes, Alex picked up a cloth used to wipe down the machine guns and gently, he wiped the blood and tears from Frank's face. Alex walked Frank away from the Horse and stayed with him until he calmed down. Thirty minutes later, the Horse lifted from the runway heading for Schweinfurt, Germany, on mission number 17.

Frank shivered as the memory of the sight ran before his eyes. The man had been talking normally, with no indication of what was to come. He had come to the base the same day as Frank, and had completed fifteen missions. Frank thought he had known him well, but apparently not well enough to have known what was on his mind. He wished he could have done something to help.

The mission to Schweinfurt was to bomb a ball-bearing factory, but all Frank could think about was the man at the airplane. Every event of the mission blurred in his mind; it all ran together, the flak, the fighters, the bombs dropping, all just a jumbled mess in his memory.

As the Horse hit the tarmac on the return to base, all Frank knew was that everyone on his crew, including the new navigator, had returned without injury.

Frank was still nauseated when he reached the mess hall. The OIC with the whiskey must have seen the look on Frank's face and slipped him an extra shot of Scotch. Even that did not stop the memory from tracing before his mind's eye as he sat without touching his food. Only Frank had seen the accident first hand. The others on his crew had asked a lot of questions that Frank could not answer without choking up. They stopped their inquiry as they saw the effects and realized what a gory sight it must have been.

He was so upset he really did not know what to do. King suggested that he should go see the flight surgeon, but there was no way Frank was going to do that. He thought he would be grounded and that was the last thing he wanted. If the surgeon saw his heel, and the taped leg, along with how he was reacting to the latest development, it would be the hospital for him and he knew it.

A slight drizzle had started to fall when Frank walked out of the hut, but he paid no attention to how wet he was getting as he walked. How long he walked he did not know, but when he raised his head and looked up, there was the mansion—Ashly's home. Darkness had fallen and here he stood at this place. Three miles he had walked and all he thought about was the man at the airplane. He must have been trying to walk it off in his stupor. He felt screwed up in the head and turned to walk away, but someone in the house must have looked out and seen him standing there in the rain because the butler came running out with an umbrella and held it over his head.

"Sergeant Mays, what are you doing out in this rain?"

"Hello, Charles. I was out walking and got caught in the rain so I decided to come here," he lied.

"You are drenched. Quick, let me get you in the house before you catch a cold."

Feeling dumb, Frank walked under the umbrella with Charles to the side door and tried to shake some of the water from his clothes. He began to shiver as if cold, but he knew the warm summer rain was not the problem. He hoped that something warm to drink would help.

Dame Metcalf and Ashly were waiting at the door. Aunt Amy said, "Quick, get inside so you can be dried."

"I'm soaked and I'm afraid I'll ruin your floor."

"Don't be silly. This floor has been wet many times. Ashly, go get a towel and a blanket to wrap him in. He must be dried or he may catch a cold. Charles, make some hot tea and bring it here."

Frank had not been fussed over like this since he was a small child, and it felt good to hear someone concerned for him.

"Frank, let me wrap you with this," Ashly said, holding a blanket toward him.

He looked at her for the first time and her mouth dropped, but she did not say a word. She apparently noticed that something was drastically wrong with him, but realized that now was not the time to inquire.

Charles brought hot tea with a slice of lemon. *Lemon!* Frank had not seen a slice of lemon for months. A lemon here in England was unheard of. Charles took the towel and began drying Frank's hair.

"Let me do that, please," Ashly said, taking the towel from Charles.

Frank emptied the teacup and when he bit the slice of lemon, his mouth reacted to the tartness and he laughed at himself.

"He'll be all right now," said Ashly. "I'll take him upstairs and get this wet clothing off so it'll dry. Charles, please come up and take the clothes and dry them."

In her room, Ashly helped remove Frank's clothes and prepared a hot tub bath. She then washed his body as if he were a baby, and dried him the same way. Warm and dry, he lay rolled in a blanket on her bed.

"You would make a fine nurse," he told Ashly as she sat beside him. "You really know how to bathe and dry a fellow. I like your gentle touch."

Ashly asked what had happened to cause him to be out walking in the rain and he could think of no way out of answering her question, so he told the story as cleanly as he could, leaving out the gory details. Ashly indicated how badly she felt for him and asked if he could stay with her. She held him tightly to her breast and kissed him.

"Like I told you, I just walked around in the rain so I don't have a pass. No one knows where I am and they may be searching for me. I don't want to be AWOL. Are my fatigues dry? I have to go back."

Charles brought the dried and pressed fatigues and Frank quickly put them on. He had just finished dressing when Charles again rapped on the door.

"Miss Ashly, there's a military vehicle outside.

They've come to take Sergeant Mays back to base."

"All right, Charles, tell them we'll be down in a minute."

Ashly hugged and kissed Frank, looking at him as never before. "I do not like letting you go like this," she said.

Downstairs, Frank found Alex waiting at the door. "Frank, I had to come and get you. Our names are on the list for tomorrow's mission."

"We understand," Ashly said as she kissed Frank's cheek. "Take good care of him so he can return to me soon."

Frank thanked Aunt Amy and Charles for their help and walked to the waiting jeep with Alex, while Charles held an umbrella over his head. In the covered jeep, Frank was bursting to ask Alex some questions as to how he found him.

"Where the hell did you get a jeep and how did you know where to find me?"

"We soldiers have to take care of our buddies, you know."

"Hell, that's not an answer. Tell me!"

"I meant what I said, and the jeep came from in front of HQ, courtesy of the First Sergeant—he just doesn't know it yet. Don't you think I keep up with you and your girlfriends? Lieutenant Swartz told me where you might be. So here I am. Anything else you want to know?"

"Yes. How the hell did you handle the accident so well this morning?"

"Remember, I just knew that guy casually, and I really was not watching until someone yelled. And, I wasn't the one with blood all over me."

"Okay, asshole! I really do appreciate your thoughtfulness and you are my best friend. Okay? Thanks a bunch."

"Hey, we've had some good times together and I think I may have broken before now if it hadn't been for your support. We really are two of a kind, you know. We have to look out for each other."

"You're right, old fart, we are two of a kind—a pair of screw-ups of sorts. We all need a little help now and then. I really should've stayed and talked this out with you, but instead I acted like an asshole and went to Ashly. Thanks for coming to get me."

Alex just looked at Frank and smiled. There was an unspoken language among true friends and no more had to be said.

Frank wondered why Ashly never asked about the adhesive tape all over his right leg. He knew she must have wondered how he hurt it, but she didn't question him as to what had happened.

Alex drove the jeep through the gate and parked it in front of HQ. The rain had stopped, meaning the mission for tomorrow would be a go.

At 3:00 a.m., the CQ rolled them out of their sacks. "On your feet, soldiers," he yelled, as all in the hut were on the list to fly today's mission. Somebody threw a shoe at him as he ran out the door. Yeah, he could laugh; he didn't have to face the crap today.

July 20, 1944, Mission number 18, D-Day + 44. Target: Oil Depot located at Merseburg, Germany. Bombs: twenty 250-pounders. Altitude: 26,000 feet.

This mission was like so many others. The target

was defended with several anti-aircraft guns and the flak was relentless. German ME-109s attacked at several points along the way. The formation was chewed up from the time they crossed the coast of Germany.

The group had started out with P-51 fighter escort, but the fighters returned home before the Germans attacked. It sure looked as if the Germans had the complete flight plan for this mission. They seemed to know every move the formation of B-17s was going to make and were waiting for them. There had to be a spy at Great Ashfield for this information to get into their hands. Whoever was letting out the information was causing the deaths of many airmen.

Frank had fired his twin .50-caliber machine guns until he was almost out of ammunition. He did not have a confirmed kill yet, but the action was so fast no one could keep up with who shot down what. It really did not matter who got credit for downing a German.

When the 385th returned to base that afternoon, they had been in the air for seven-and-a-half hours. The airplanes were carrying many dead and wounded, but Frank didn't plan attending any more funerals. What mattered most was that the target had been destroyed and no one in Frank's hut was lost or injured. The shot of Scotch whiskey was a welcome gift to his empty stomach but the food still did not set well.

Another day, another combat mission. The next morning the crews were in a briefing and the officer said today's target was to help the "Mud-Hogs" in the trenches in France. The group was to bomb the German defense lines in front of the American ground troops. The news that they were going directly to help the American troops brought a cheer from the airmen, as this was a job they most welcomed anytime.

Frank noted on his scrap paper: Monday, July 24, 1944, Mission number 19, D-Day + 48. Target: St. Lo, France.

The Horse carried her crew up into a freshly washed sky. She smelled like a lady of the night from all the stale cigarette smoke lingering in the air. The mission was short and when the bomb bay doors opened at the sight of the green signal flares on the ground, 1300 100-pound bombs plowed the area. Frank watched the bombs create their devastation around the target and imagined many men were dying in the holocaust below.

There was little flak and not one German fighter appeared. It was a true *milk run* and not a single airman was injured. The formation circled from St. Lo back over the English Channel, and once there, Frank cleared his guns and crawled into the waist of the Horse. He sat back and lit a cigarette, thinking how lucky he had been on these missions and wondering how many men had been killed on the ground in the rain of bombs.

Back at base, the crew attended a debriefing where they were told there might have been a problem on this mission, but that the Brass would have to clear the information. The men could not understand what the problem might be as bombs were dropped in the target zone and no bombers had been lost.

It was lunchtime when the crew entered the mess hall. The odor of food still made Frank's stomach feel queasy. There had to be a problem with his stomach but he did not have a clue as to the cause. He had begun to eat very little food and was losing weight. The ration of Scotch whiskey was no longer working as it had in the beginning. He lay on his bunk for the balance of the day.

The next morning in briefing they learned the bad news. The Germans had retreated the day before and the anxious American troops had followed them into the bomb drop zone. This meant they had bombed their own troops. Again, it seemed the Germans had word of the mission plan and had suckered the Americans into a trap. The holocaust had resulted in many American soldiers being killed and wounded.

Today's mission was a rerun of the one from the day before, except that the American troops held their positions and the Germans rioted as the American forces made a big advance on the entire front. This counted as Mission number 20, D-Day +49, in Frank's notes. There were no airplanes lost or men injured.

Frank looked to the west on their return from St. Lo and saw clouds moving in over England. This weather front could prevent flying, as the clouds were ominously black.

Back at the mess hall, Alex had something to say about how little Frank was eating. "Off you're feed, country boy?"

"Yeah, I think I'm pregnant."

"Let's get away and go to London if we can get a pass."

Frank would rather have gone to see Ashly, but instead, he mumbled, "Okay, if that's what you want to do." No way would Frank have disappointed Alex and not have gone to London with him.

The following morning the weather had socked-in all of England, so getting a pass was no problem and soon Alex and Frank were on the train headed to London. Frank told Alex about Nichole having a small apartment and that she would want Frank to stay with her.

"That's no problem. I can stay at the club," Alex said.

Frank thought of Ashly's soft bed and how he enjoyed being with her. She made such a fuss over him, making him feel as if he were somebody. She would rub his back and help relax the muscles tight from tension. Sometimes she would hold his head in her lap, gently caress his hair and sing a soft lullaby. He ate it up like a spoiled brat.

Frank did not want Alex to sleep at the club while he was sharing Nichole's soft bed, and said, "Let's see what works out before you make that choice."

"Hell, Frank, I don't mind. Maybe I'll get lucky and go home with one of the volunteers."

"Let's go see Nichole first," Frank suggested, thinking that maybe she would have an idea to solve the problem.

"Okay by me. Whatever you say."

Alex and Frank talked the entire 90-mile train ride to London. Both had become aware there was little chance of finishing all their missions. Alex was not as skeptical as Frank about pending doom, but the deaths of Lieutenant Butt and all Frank's other friends had him resigned to his own death. He needed all the slack time away from the base that he could get to live the little life he thought he had left.

Alex had learned from Frank and he made hardly any friends at all. He stayed clear of getting too close to anyone and that helped him to deal with all the lost airmen better than Frank was handling it.

The train finally backed into Paddington Station and they debarked, ready for a good time. The low clouds made the city seem darker than usual, but Alex and Frank were deliriously happy just to be away from the base.

CHAPTER 14

Rainy Days and Rest

The rain was pouring in London and the streets were bare of people. The weather, however, did not deter Alex and Frank at all. It was a welcome sight because it meant they did not have to fly. They rode a taxi to the Red Cross Club and found Nichole working there, so they sat around waiting for her to check out.

Frank told her that he did not want Alex to stay at the Club and asked if she knew what they could do so that Alex would have fun. He asked if she knew any girls with whom she might get Alex a date and Nichole rang-up a girl she knew. The girl, who's name was Dana, told Nichole that she would be delighted to date Alex and all arrangements were made to go get her.

They met the girl named Dana at the restaurant owned by Nichole's relatives. Dana was the same age as Alex: twenty-one years old. Alex looked as if he had never seen a girl as pretty as Dana Blair, and she seemed to like him too. She gave Frank a kiss on his cheek and he saw Nichole frown. He knew she was jealous and did not want to share her time with anyone.

Then came eating, drinking, hugging and kissing, but not all in that order. Frank ate very little and did not drink anything, as something was still amiss with his stomach. After discussing where to stay, they decided Nichole's place was too cramped for four people. Frank wanted no part of spending his time with Nichole while another couple was in the room, as it might spoil all his pleasure. Dana finally explained that she had a place of her own, which was larger than Nichole's flat, and she wanted all of them to go there.

When the girls went to the ladies' room and Frank was alone with Alex, he asked, "What do you think, Buddy? Do you like her? Bet she could make you happy."

"I believe she will, my friend, but that remains to be seen."

"Speaking of being seen. Four in one bed?"

Alex laughed a real belly laugh. "That had not crossed my mind. Damn, I don't know. What'd you think?"

"I expect we'll have to split. I like you a lot, but I'm not sure I want you in bed with me."

Alex, already laughing, almost split a gut he laughed so hard. "With four in a bed, it would be hard to know who you're doing it to."

When the girls returned they wanted to know what was so funny. This did not help the situation because now Frank had started laughing as hard as Alex, and it took a few minutes for both to regain their composure. Nichole was obviously unhappy at the unknown joke and became upset with Frank, demanding to know what was going on. Frank noticed she was upset with him and wanted to set things straight, but that would have to wait until they were alone.

"I'll tell you all about it in a while. Trust me until I stop laughing."

Nichole said flatly, "Dana and Alex will stay at her

place."

The rain continued to fall in a steady drizzle as Nichole and Frank took a taxi to her flat. Taxi service in London was the finest Frank had ever experienced. The old cars were grand to ride in and the drivers were reasonably well mannered. Since gas was difficult to come by, most people rode the underground or busses as they traveled about the city.

Nichole was quiet during the ride and Frank thought he knew why. He had some explaining to do concerning the laughter. "I've never seen you upset with me before and it makes me feel awful," he said. "I'm sorry you didn't understand Alex and me. We're such good friends that sometimes we have this thing between us, but I'm ready to explain if you're willing to listen. Okay?"

Frank went into detail explaining the reason he and Alex had such mirth over something so simple. When he was through, Nichole looked at him and smiled. "Men! Let me tell you why I became upset. Look at the situation from my viewpoint, from a female side of the situation. Dana is so pretty and I thought you two were discussing which of us you would stay with tonight. What you do not know is that Dana made a remark about you and I know she would rather have stayed with you than with Alex. You just do not know how you affect women. From the moment Dana first saw you, she picked up on your charm. I saw it and then the remark she made to me set me up for what I thought as I entered the room. I had already made sure the four of us would not stay in one place tonight. I am very jealous of you. Do you have any clue as to what I'm saying?"

"I think I understand how you saw the situation, at

least part of it, but I don't know what you mean when you talk about this thing you call my charm."

The taxi stopped, Frank paid the fare with a nice tip and they stood for a minute in the rain just looking at each other and smiling. When they realized just how wet they were getting, they raced for the door to her flat. Once in her room they had to remove their clothes and hang them over the tub to dry. Frank thought this not a bad deal, as it might get things started sooner than he had expected.

With all lights off, the blackout drapes had been pulled back letting the rain-cleansed night air whiff across the bed. It still was not enough to keep Frank from producing a large volume of perspiration as he rolled over and lay on his back. A small puddle of sweat had formed in his solar-plexus dimple.

He felt Nichole's long blond hair brushing over his side and to his belly. In the dim light, he could see her as she gently kissed his chest. She seemed to taste of the sweat.

His curiosity forced him to ask, "What was that all about?"

"I just wanted to find out something. I've questioned it for some time."

"What?"

"I tasted your sweat to find out if it was the same as your odor," she said with a smile on her face.

"Okay, I give up. Now I really don't understand."

"There's something I'm sure you're completely unaware of and I probably shouldn't tell you. But you should know. You have something—a gift as old as man—and you have combined this gift with a personality that sets females in a sexual frenzy. Most women do not know what turns them on to a man. They just know it happens. The Greeks have known this for many centuries. Your body produces an odor along with your sweat that is attractive to women. That's what happened when Dana met you and I certainly was not about to tell her. A man's natural odor is meant to attract females, but some men try to attract women by applying artificial scents, and in so doing, they cover this natural odor. It works for some females but turns others off when a man does not smell right. Don't ever do anything to change whatever it is you do now."

Nichole looked at Frank and seeing that he was listening intently, she decided to continue with her description of what she thought was a truth.

"You do not use after-shave lotion, colognes, hair oils or any other scents that hide your odor. This erogenous odor is you. Combined with your nice smile and lighthearted personality, this makes you appear to females as if you are seeking a mate and they unknowingly respond. That's why you seem to stand out in a crowd. You constantly cast this personality. Some males will respond also and never know why, since it's a lost function among most men. When you become sexually aroused, these things multiply in strength. Clean sweat on a clean body is not repulsive; it's alluring. Why do you think the ancient warriors wore little clothing? Think about it. They learned how to confuse their enemy with their natural odor. Clothing causes sweat to form a bad odor—a repulsive odor that angers, and anger causes one to act without thinking. I hope this is clear to you and does not cause me to lose you."

Frank could not prevent his mind from rerunning some events in his life concerning females that had puzzled him. "I think I understand what you said. Come to me now that I may know what you say is true."

He grinned as Nichole responded with active pleasure and he thought, "Ha, I probably smell like a bar of Lifebuoy soap."

A German air raid in a nearby neighborhood kept them awake for part of the night but only gave them more time to test Nichole's theory. When the all-clear sirens sounded, they lay quietly until sleep came to them. Frank did not have the usual nightmares and rested well. The warm, bright morning sun fell across their bodies and awakened them. It had been a long time since the sun caught Frank in bed and he enjoyed the additional sleep after the end of the air raid.

He felt good and a silly question crossed his mind, "I wonder how the stinky people spent *their* night?"

With the sun of a new day lighting their bodies, Frank wondered if the odor thing continued to be a factor in lovemaking after last night? He decided discretion was the better part of valor and headed for the bath while Nichole slept. Before leaving the base, he had stopped by and had a medic at the hospital take the tape off his leg. Skin and hair was missing and hot water stung like crazy, causing the leg to redden as he washed with soap. The old saying was: *It will get well before you get married.* Well, that would probably never happen, so he was probably in for big trouble.

Frank walked naked from the bathroom. It fit in his mind well now that nudity was not the awful thing he had been taught back home. He felt free from shame and free from feeling insecure about his body. God had given him this body, the same as Adam's, so it could not be all bad to let someone see it. In fact, if Adam hadn't eaten that damned apple and gotten smart, the world might have been in better shape now. He decided he would not eat any more apples, if ever he saw one again.

His noise in the bathroom had awakened Nichole and she had drawn the window shade and was sitting on the bed, watching as he came through the door.

"Please. Just stand there for a minute and let me feast my eyes on my Apollo."

"Your Greek god Zeus tells me I must obey your command," Frank said. He stopped, turned around with his arms above his head then dropped them to the stance of a stature of David he had once seen.

Nichole rolled back on the bed laughing at his antics and exposed her undulating body as she made room for him to sit beside her. Frank kissed her shoulder as he caressed her beautiful naked body.

Quickly wrapping a robe around herself, Nichole got up and said, "Not now, sir. I must adjourn for a few minutes."

Frank knew where the clean sheets were kept so he stripped the bed and remade it before Nichole returned from the bathroom. He neatly folded the soiled linen and placed it in a chair.

"You didn't have to do that," she said when she returned.

"I know. I was just passing time before I dress."

"When did you learn to square sheets that way?"

"Madam, the Army teaches many things. I do this with Army blankets every time I get out of bed."

He saw that Nichole had started to dress and he began putting on his clothes also. He had seen the soiled sheets and knew Nichole had a reason to dress this early. She was definitely not pregnant. Then his mind returned to Ashly. If his morning sickness was not because of Nichole, he wondered whether Ashly was all right.

"We are to have breakfast with Dana and your Alex this morning. They should be here by now."

"*My* Alex?"

"You two are very close."

"But, *my* Alex?"

"I've never had a friend as close as you have in Alex."

"Okay, I'll buy that. We really are close. I said once I would never let anyone get close to me again. It's happened before, but no more. But I lied. He's a great guy and it would kill me if something happened to him."

Frank did not know if he should tell Nichole what he'd found out about her sister. Why should he? It would probably only hurt her more. Her sister was alive and seemed to be safe for the time being, so he finally reasoned it best left alone, as Nichole seemed to have forgotten about it.

Nichole pressed Frank's clothing and he finished dressing as they listened to the radio. The weather outside had made a slight change for the better. Soon Dana and Alex were knocking at the door and that stopped Frank's thinking about Nichole and her sister.

After greetings and a short walk, they arrived at the restaurant that Dana had selected. The clouds had opened to allow the morning sunshine but had now closed again and the sky was gray.

The restaurant was a small place. Frank looked

around and thought the place must have been this way for the past hundred or more years. A typical English breakfast frequently consisted of baked beans, cheese toast and tea, but Frank conned his way into a pot of strong black coffee. It had to be from the black market as coffee was difficult to find in England. It cost Frank an extra ten shillings but it was worth every pence. He sat back and enjoyed the coffee, and noticed Dana seemed to enjoy it also. Nichole was not much of a coffee drinker.

When the girls left for the restroom, Alex exploded in conversation. "Frank, Dana is the salt of the earth. She's something to behold. You can't believe what a good time we had. I don't want to be too descriptive but you already know what I'm trying to say. She's the best I've ever had in my life. I hardly slept an hour last night and I feel like I should take a nap . . . but I'm afraid I'll miss something. Know what I mean?"

"I'd say you not only got your ashes hauled but had the whole damn bin cleaned out."

"You got that right! Damn, it felt great! Why haven't you dragged me down here with you before? I kidded you about Nichole, but never again. I think I'm in love."

Frank sat back, let out a real belly laugh and said, "You mean you're more pleased than you were with the farm girls? You said the same thing about them."

"Farm girls, hell! Sell the farm! I'm gonna plant all my seeds here in old London Town. Dana is the girl for me. I mean it when I say I think I'm in love. We talked half the night and we think so much alike, I'm sure of what I say."

The girls returned, cutting short any more of Alex's comments. Frank watched Nichole as she talked with

Dana, wondering if there would be any hint of confrontation. There was none and Nichole seemed pleased Dana was so all over Alex.

Nichole had noticed that Frank limped as he walked, and wanted to know what was wrong. He told her that he hurt it playing ball and dared not tell her that he had flown two missions with it taped. Alex backed his story and added nothing to it.

They spent most of the day in Hyde Park listening to the various orators speaking on every subject imaginable. Later they stopped by the American Bar, which stocked American whiskey, and Frank decided to get a drink. After a few minutes, the girls said they wanted to leave. Frank had seen Nichole snap at one of the ladies when she approached Frank and started talking to him. He imagined that Nichole wanted to leave because she was jealous and didn't want to risk letting him get away from her.

The foursome then went to the Greek restaurant and ordered squab under glass. Alex and Frank joked that there were four fewer pigeons crapping on the Queen's statue and she should thank them. Later they stopped at a photo shop nearby and nothing would do but for Frank to have a picture made. He ordered three copies, one each for Nichole and Ashly and one for himself. It seemed that no matter where he went or what he was doing, Ashly remained near the front of his mind.

Dana told Nichole that she and Alex were going to her apartment to rest a while before Alex and Frank had to leave. They had to be at Paddington Station to catch the 6:00 p.m. train to Stowmarket and agreed to meet later. This seemed to suit Nichole just fine, as she appeared to want Frank all to herself. Nichole asked Frank to go to her place, as she felt tired and wanted to rest. The Germans had bombed Paddington Station during the night and they had lost sleep because the station was not far from Nichole's flat. Perhaps the air raid had upset Nichole and that had caused her to start her period early.

There was little to do in her flat so they stretched out on the bed and listened to the radio. The music had a calming effect and they both napped briefly. Peaceful rest was something Frank needed most and with Nichole, he seemed to manage to find inner peace.

Later, Nichole said, "I'm glad Dana and Alex seem so right for each other. She's been such a lonely person."

"Yeah, I'm glad for them both," he replied.

"I thought you were mad at me this morning when I saw the look on your face. I am jealous, you know."

"It's okay, Nichole, I understand."

"It seems Dana has met her man. She's eaten up with Alex and I do not have to concern myself any longer with her flirting with you. We have so little time together, Frank, and I don't want to share you with anyone. I don't like to think what it would be like without you."

The rest of the day passed quickly and soon they were off to meet Dana and Alex at the station. Frank thought he might have to pull Alex away from Dana and was glad to see his buddy so happy. Frank waited on the train while Alex said his goodbyes. Alex was almost left behind at the station and had to run to catch the train.

CHAPTER 15

The Air War Continues

Alex and Frank lay around in their bunks, satisfied with their latest trip to London. Alex was in *hog heaven*, but another mission loading list was posted and the crew was scheduled to go again.

Monday, July 31, 1944, Mission number 21, D-Day + 55. This mission was to go back to Munich with the target being a railroad repair shop. The Germans were moving a mass of military supplies by rail and this shop was a source of their ability to keep the trains moving. The bomb load was a surprise: five 1000-pounders. They were told the Germans had built many thick concrete buildings and it would take this weight bomb to penetrate the structures.

Going to the target, they picked up a German fighter that had a new trick up his sleeve. The fighter stayed out of machine gun range, level with the formation of bombers and radioed their altitude to the ground gunners. Now every time they neared an anti-aircraft battery, the Germans knew their altitude and put their shells dead in the center of the formation of B-17s. This was cutting the bombers to pieces and two had to return to base with damaged engines. Frank doubted they would make it home as they were so deep in German air space. German fighters were always in the skies whenever they saw one or two B-17s by themselves because out of formation, a B-17 had little chance against a fighter.

As the group approached the point to start the bomb run, thick flak appeared ahead of the formation. In their briefings, they had been told the target would be defended by more than 500 anti-aircraft guns, which all appeared to be in working order. Frank looked ahead and thought, "No way in hell can we get through this alive."

Then and there, Frank *made peace with his God.*

The hellish puffs of black smoke from the bursting shells mixed with flashes of dirty red flame as they exploded, each burst a deadly scattering of hundreds of pieces of hot, sharp metal. The shape of each burst looked to Frank like a piece of black popcorn and soon the sky became filled with this black image such that he could not see the earth through the dense smoke.

With a timer, the Germans could set any altitude for the 88-millimeter shell and they knew how much time was required for a shell to travel to the target once it left the barrel of the anti-aircraft gun. The detonator in the nose of the shell was set for both altitude and impact. The Germans generally used a five-gun battery and the shells were set to explode within a split second of each other.

With several hundred anti-aircraft guns surrounding an area, the number of exploding shells was awesome. Each gun could fire every twenty seconds, so 500 guns could put 1500 shells per minute into a formation of bombers. The result was devastating when the formation made a three-to-four minute bombing run. It was like living in hell with the furnaces going full blast. The smoke did not dissipate quickly, leaving the residue to appear as a large black cloud. The bombers flew through the mass of scattering shrapnel and it cut into the aluminum bodies

of the airplanes with a sound the airmen learned to call
flak.

Shells began to explode next to the Horse and
shrapnel ripped through the bomber. The sound of
exploding shells and flak cutting through the metal body
of the plane unnerved the airmen, who knew that death's
door was full open this day and many would step through.

Frank spun his turret, hoping to deflect the hot shards
of metal. This was his only defense at this point. He
thought, "Where are you now, Guardian Angel?"

The formation of B-17s had no more than entered
the flak barrage when one of the Horse's wing planes
received a direct hit, rolled over, and dived toward earth.
Frank did not see a single parachute leaving the airplane.
Then suddenly their left wing plane went under his ball
turret and rolled slightly, nose-dived downward, then
exploded with only small pieces falling away. Not one
parachute came from that bomber either.

The sound of shrapnel hitting the Horse sounded as
if someone were throwing gravel on a tin roof. Frank
turned his turret and saw the bomb bay doors opening.
When they were fully open, the bombs dropped and he
counted the five bombs away then reported his count to
the bombardier.

Then he heard the pilot telling the co-pilot to feather
number 1 engine propeller, and as he looked under the
left wing, Frank saw black oil streaming from the
damaged engine.

As quickly as it started the flak stopped as they flew
out of range of the defense guns. Frank realized they
were in the flak area for about four minutes and estimated
some 6,000 shells had burst in and around the formation

of B-17s. He looked down at the target area and saw the bombs bursting as they strung along to and beyond the target.

Then he saw a huge building with a Red Cross clearly painted on the roof. The bombs began to burst closer to this building, and then it happened—the Red Cross was no more! The entire building, which could have been a hospital, exploded and became a cloud of burning dark smoke. The explosion seemed more intense than one would expect of a hospital building and Intelligence would later claim it was not in fact a hospital but a part of the factory storage and munitions. Of course, several 1,000-pound bombs could make one hell of a blast, so Frank was never sure what was inside the building. From his ball turret, it sure had looked like a hospital, and it was outside the defensive anti-aircraft gun area.

Naturally, the Germans later claimed it *was* a hospital!

The return trip from Munich was about the same as going in, but the formation picked up an American fighter escort of P-51s halfway home. The Mustangs seemed to mother two straggling B-17s that were trailing far behind the formation. No matter if the escort was with them, Frank kept a watch for German fighters from his ball turret. As had happened before, the Germans sometimes sent several fighters to draw away the escort, and then others would hit the formation. B-17s were an easy target for German fighters if they could break through the gunner's machine-gun fire. The bombers were big and slow moving, going only about 160 miles per hour, whereas the fighters flew at over 300 mph.

As the formation crossed the coast of England, Frank cleared his guns and crawled from the turret. Still at

18,000 feet and lowering, he started to remove his oxygen mask, and as he did, it ripped skin from his face. Moisture from his breath had frozen the edges of the mask to his face. This was the second or third time it had happened to him.

King and Alex joined Frank in the waist and they lit cigarettes without saying a word. Frank knew what was on Alex's mind: Dana. He looked at Frank and smiled a sneaky grin. Most of the time, neither had to say a word, as they knew what the other was thinking. One would have thought they were both crazy, sitting there looking at each other as they took a long drag, blew it out and put the mask back on to breathe.

The airplanes began to circle Great Ashfield, now down to 2,000 feet and lowering, waiting for the badly damaged to get on the runway first. Alex put his fur-lined booted feet up high on the fuselage, turned his head to Frank, grinned and said, "Frank, we really are a pair. I've just begun to live. I was about to let life pass me by when we went to London."

The crew of the Horse was not allowed to leave the base and it was taking longer to repair the airplanes than had been expected. Getting spare parts seemed to be a real problem. On August 2, they went on their next mission, to take out an airport near Paris. Frank had checked and rechecked everything on the Horse. He still had not shaken the image of Lieutenant Butt's death on that other mission to Paris. He did not fear the mission, but that certain feeling came over him whenever Paris was mentioned. Between that mission and his friend walking into the propeller, he was almost a basket case.

The mission turned out all right, as the airfield was destroyed and no one on the Horse was injured. Frank managed to shoot down another ME-109 and that brightened his outlook as he returned to base from mission number 22, D-Day + 57.

Again the crew was restricted to base and no one knew why. Alex was chomping at the bit to return to Dana, but it would not be this day. Frank tried to get a pass to go see Ashly, but without any luck. He wondered if Swartz was keeping her informed. He had not seen Swartz for about a week and thought he must be taking care of his woman over at the mansion. Frank still had not found out if Swartz was a married man. He really didn't care, he was just curious.

Frank caught up on some letters to people back in the States, played poker and shot some latrine craps, winning a few pounds. It was not satisfying him to do these things as he missed Ashly and her majestic ways. He did not understand why he was so lonely without her. Even when he was with Nichole, he thought mostly of Ashly. He had never felt this way before about a girl and asked himself why he found so much difference between them, since they both treated him so well. He had a picture to give Ashly and it couldn't be delivered. He wished his stomach would let up from this sickness that he felt most of the time. He and Alex kept each other company, as the rest of the crew lay in their bunks all the time.

A thought kept running through Frank's mind that it had been only 58 days since his first mission and his next flight would be his twenty-third mission. He was averaging a mission every three days! This had to be some sort of record, but who other than him was keeping count? At this rate, he would get in his twenty-fifth mission before his twentieth birthday. That is, if he remained lucky enough to live that long.

The wait was finally over and the crew was slated to fly again. Friday, August 4, 1944, Mission number 23, D-Day + 59. Target: Oil storage. Location: Hamburg, Germany. Bombs: twelve 500-pound general demolition. Altitude 24,000 feet. Estimated time of flight: 7-1/2 hours. Oxygen: 3-1/2 hours.

The briefing officer said this was a German U-boat nest and they were to stop the supply of fuel to the subs. The target was located on the coast of northwest Germany and would be defended by the Germans with heavy flak and lots of fighters. Frank was told he might get to see some of the German FW-190 fighters on this mission. All he had seen so far were the ME-109s and the FW-190 was supposed to be a better fighter airplane. Perhaps he would find out today.

The group would not have fighter escort on this mission and it was his guess that somehow the Germans knew about it. He was becoming positive there was a spy at Great Ashfield and the Germans were aware of certain missions. Some bastard was really costing the lives of many Americans. Everybody on base was alert to anyone saying anything that could be a clue as to who it was.

At 24,000 feet, the formation of bombers flew just south of Helogland in the North Sea, turned due east, and flew toward the German coast where they met heavy flak coming from the ground. The Horse bounced and jerked from the close bursting shells. As the bomb bay doors opened, the German FW-190s attacked the formation, diving after the bombers through the flak.

The German fighter pilots knew that the bomber gunners would be hunkered down while the airplanes were in the target area, and they were correct. The first wave of fighters took out two B-17s on the first run and the gunners were surprised as only the ball turret gunner was firing back. The flak was dense and accurate and a third B-17 went down. Frank saw a German fighter spiraling down but did not know if a gunner or the German's own flak had hit it. As the bombs dropped from the bomb bay, several bursting shells hit the Horse and it jerked upward from the blast.

Numbers 2 and 3 engines died suddenly, as if someone had cut off the switch. The co-pilot feathered the two propellers while the pilot tried to control the airplane. The Horse was losing altitude fast and was not yet clear of the flak zone. Shells continued to burst nearby, causing further damage as the airplane fell. An FW-190 at 9 o'clock made a pass at the Horse and Alex and Frank made short work of shooting him down. Then for some unknown reason, the fighters broke off the attack and were gone. The Horse was an easy target as the airplane was now alone without defense from the formation, so it made no sense for the Germans not to continue with the attack.

The mission had been a disaster as Frank had seen four B-17s go down and many others were damaged. As they exited the flak area, the others left the Horse behind and it continued to lose altitude. The number 1 engine had been damaged and it was running rough.

Frank questioned what would happen next? Could

the Horse make it home on two engines? Yes, no problem, but what if number 1 engine were to quit? No one on the airplane wanted to consider what would happen if they had to ditch in the North Sea. The water temperature was one thing, but being captured by the Germans was something else.

The navigator told the pilot it was the same distance from here to Sweden as to the base, with both routes being over water. German ships would defend the way to Sweden by sea, so there was no question the pilot would try to get the Horse back to Great Ashfield. If they could distance themselves far enough from the German coast, there was a chance the Air/Sea Rescue could save them, assuming the Horse had to ditch in the North Sea. It was a long-shot gamble, but seemed the only one they had.

The pilot gave the order to lighten the airplane by throwing all removable items overboard. Now down to 5,000 feet and losing altitude fast with over 100 miles to go, they stripped the Horse of everything. *Everything*! All guns, ammo, the radio after the last *mayday* was transmitted, all personal bags, portable oxygen bottles, spent shell casings, parachutes, parachute harnesses, nonessential emergency equipment, fur-lined flight suits, all went into the North Sea.

Since they had no reply, they were not sure if rescue had received their emergency message. Gas was transferred from the right wing tanks to the left wing number 1 fuel tank. The pilot was able to raise the right wing slightly but the number 1 engine was sputtering almost off at times and the Horse was losing airspeed. It was a fight for the pilots to manage the flight path.

Now down to 800 feet and no rescue boats or coastline was in sight as the horse continued to lose altitude. However, there was a surprise gift as the warmer water added some lift to the airplane. The Horse was now holding at 600 feet with forty miles to go over water, and everyone questioned whether they were going to make those last few miles? It really did not seem possible the Horse could stay in the air that length of time and for that many miles.

As it seemed there was no way to prevent ditching in the North Sea, the crewmen gathered in the waist and discussed how to keep their cigarettes and matches dry. The tail gunner produced a handfuls of condoms, which he used as kneepads in the knee pockets of his flight suit, and this brought a round of belly laughter from the gunners. They wanted to know what his plans were if he ever got shot down over Germany. Was he planning on *screwing* his way back to England? It was funny, but at least the smokes and matches would stay dry now.

They discussed whether they should drop the ball turret but decided the hole it would leave in the bottom of the airplane would cause them to sink even faster, so the turret stayed. They considered every option, even to dismantling the tail-wheel assembly and dropping the wheel.

They were down to 300 feet when the pilot came over the intercom and reported the English coast was in sight. All jumped to see and sure enough, the Horse had made it over the North Sea to land. Good Girl!

After crossing the coastline, number 1 engine quit running and the right wing dipped, requiring the pilots to pull the plane level using ailerons. Now at 200 feet, with only one engine running, they flew just above the treetops, their air speed at 120 mph, with still ten miles to go. They had no choice but to try to make it home, as there was no place to land between here and there.

With everyone in crash positions, the pilot keyed his mike and said the only way was straight in on any runway that came in sight. The airplane was wobbling as the pilots tried to maintain control and stretch all the Horse had in her. The airplane was vibrating as if it would come apart at any second. The six crewmen were sitting with their backs to the forward wall of the radio room, all in a mass, ready to take the coming crash. Suddenly, there came the sound of tires screeching as they hit on the tarmac. The wheels had just made the end of the runway and had they hit in the grass, they would have dug-in and crashed the airplane.

Sometime later, when Frank heard the song, he thought about his returning, "On A Wing and A Prayer."

So, what did the Air Corps think they were made of? Their airplane could not fly, so why should they? Someone had decided the crew of the Horse should not lay around and think of the mission to Hamburg, so to keep them healthy, they had to fly! That night their names appeared on the loading list for tomorrow morning.

August 5, Mission number 24, D-Day + 60. This morning found the crew sitting beside a borrowed airplane. A man had been killed on this plane the day before and the crew had been grounded, but the aircraft had received only slight damage.

Frank wondered how one plane could get shot to pieces with nobody injured, while the other only received slight damage and someone was killed. It didn't make sense. Then the Brass decided to put his crew through the crap a second day, as if they didn't give a damn about the men.

It was Saturday morning and Alex came to Frank with a lot of conversation. "I sure was counting on having the weekend off so I could go to London. After yesterday I know the Army don't give a shit for us one damn bit."

"You've been reading my mind again, smart ass."

"Hell, it don't take a mind reader to know what's on your mind. You've got Ashly on the brain old boy, just like I've got Dana in the same place, fart-head."

"I could tell what you're thinking without a brain. I've found out where your brain is and it ain't above your belt," Frank responded as he slapped Alex on the backside.

"Yeah. Ain't it nice to satisfy your brain and not have to use it?"

The two buddies laughed and lit cigarettes. The cool morning air bit through Frank's longjohns and he began donning his flight suit.

"Get your asses on board," King yelled to Alex and Frank as the pilots started the engines. The borrowed B-17 then rolled from the hardstand on the taxi strip, without a groan such as the Horse always made.

The entire crew was soon finding fault with the borrowed airplane. Koop did not like it because he was missing all the flak vests he had packed in the tail of the Horse. The pilot was having trouble trimming the airplane for level flight. The bombardier said something about all the blood had not been cleaned from his seat. The bombardier had been the one killed in the airplane the previous day. Frank found the ball turret was a newer model, but the controls were similar and the ammo storage held more rounds of ammunition than his old turret.

The 385th was on its way to Magdeburg, Germany with an estimated flight time of 8 hours roundtrip. The men had been told there would be fighter escort deep into Germany for this mission, which meant that it would be a bitch of a trip. The target was known to be defended by many 88-mm anti-aircraft guns.

All went well until the formation neared the target area. There had been some light flak along the way but nothing really damaging. "Maybe this new airplane will do a job for us and we'll get home in one piece," Frank thought.

Deep in Germany, the German ME-109s came after the bombers, but the P-51s were scouting and saw them coming. The group left the fighters in a dogfight. As the group reached the IP and started their bombing run, all hell broke loose. The Germans had been waiting until the bombers were in dead range before they opened fire. Shells began bursting right in the middle of the formation of bombers. Fortunately, this bombing run had been planned to be short, because if it had not, the mission would have been a complete disaster as the bombers were receiving many hits and men were dying.

Frank counted the bombs as they fell from the bomb bay, as bombs 1 through 9 fell clear. But then instead of number 10 falling free, they heard a loud thump, which jarred the Horse. Frank notified the bombardier of the count and Mark looked in the bomb bay to determine the problem. He confirmed that a bomb was hung and had fused, ready for explosion. Any bump and the 15-second delay fuse would blow up the bomb—and the Horse. Flak popping around the airplane added to the dangerous situation.

The pilot turned the airplane, flew off to the left of the formation and hit the emergency jump button. As the alarm sounded, Frank crawled from his turret and snapped on his parachute. All the gunners except Alex sat by the waist door with a hand on the emergency release waiting for the final jump alarm. Alex headed for the bomb bay and Frank connected his headset into the intercom system.

What he heard was a conversation between Alex and the first pilot. Alex was saying, "Sir, I think the bomb can be jettisoned but it'll be risky. It will take several men if you want to try it, and it still may blow."

"I'll radio the formation commander, standby."

After a few seconds, the pilot turned the airplane away and flew farther from the other airplanes. He said, "We've been ordered to fly out where we can be observed. Then we can do what we want. Let's take a vote on whether to bail out or attempt to jettison the bomb."

All the crew connected their intercoms and voted unanimously to get rid of the bomb. Everyone knew it was dangerous either way. This was a case of get rid of the bomb or be taken prisoner by the Germans, assuming anyone lived through the jump. Frank thought he would rather die trying than surrender to the Germans. He doubted that all of them would live through the jump and then they might be killed as soon as they reached the ground. After all ten men voted to stay with the airplane, the pilot reported their decision to the formation commander.

Frank had switched his intercom to the command radio and heard the formation commander tell the pilot, "Good luck to you boys. Be careful, we want you back home."

The command pilot had approved the decision and now came the task of the crew following through. Mark, Alex and Frank stood in the bomb bay and discussed a plan to dislodge the bomb. The rest of the crew was aware of this decision and had put their lives in the hands of the three men standing in the bomb bay. One bump on the bomb and it was all over.

The bomb bay doors were opened and with portable oxygen bottles, the three men crawled over the 500-pound bomb, Mark at the nose, Alex at the rear and Frank straddling it in the middle. Since there was limited space in the close quarters, Mark and Alex couldn't wear parachutes, so Frank, who had one on, held onto the others, one hand on Mark's harness and the other on Alex's. The idea was if one of the men slipped and was falling out of the bomb bay, Frank would let loose of one man and fall with the other, sharing a parachute made for only one person.

Cold wind whipped through the open doors and with the bomb tight against his groin, Frank thought, "What an odd-shaped hole I'm gonna cut through the top of the airplane when this sucker goes off. Just like in a movie cartoon. God, that's really gonna hurt between my legs."

The front of the bomb suddenly slipped and it fell toward the center beam of the bomb bay. If it hit, it was all over, so Mark grabbed the nose of the bomb and lifted as he swung it clear of the beam. Alex jerked loose the snagged tailfin and the bomb fell away, dropping clear and out of the bomb bay through a cloud of bursting anti-aircraft explosions below the airplane. The three expected to see the bomb hit by flak and explode, as they stood motionless, watching the bomb falling through the flak. Neither of them moved until the bomb exploded on the ground. Almost frozen, they crawled from the bomb bay and notified the pilot that all was clear.

Once again, Frank knew that he had cheated death!

The pilot notified the flight commander that everything was clear and he welcomed them back into the formation. Frank reentered his ball turret and stayed quiet the rest of the flight over Germany. When over the English Channel, Frank crawled from the turret to light a cigarette. His oxygen mask was again frozen to his face and hurt like hell as he ripped it off. The match would hardly flame at 20,000 feet. Finally, he got it lit and he would take a drag, blow it out, put the mask back on, breathe, then do it over again as he smoked the cigarette.

The next morning the crew was called to squadron HQ and taken before the base commander. In the meeting, the entire crew was awarded the *Distinguished Flying Cross* for their heroic actions the day before as they had performed *above and beyond the call of duty.*

That was the good news.

"Gentlemen, by order of General Jimmy Doolittle, the Commander in Chief, USAAF, all combat crews will be required to fly an additional ten missions, for a total of thirty-five, before being rotated home," announced the Colonel. "Thank you gentlemen, dismissed."

"Aw, shit ... well, kiss my ass ... now don't that grab you by the balls?"

What could they say? "Yes sir; thank you sir."

Frank knew the Air Corps was running short of airmen and that they had been taking huge losses in manpower. He also knew now that he was a dead man for sure. There was no way he could luck out for an additional twelve missions—no *gott dammt* way!

All that was left was kiss his ass goodbye!

Frank had to stop and review his situation. He had been in England for two months and a few days, and in that time, he had flown 24 combat missions. One man on his crew had been killed and many other buddies had died or been wounded. The sight of the deaths would not leave his mind. Totally different from that young teenager who had arrived at Great Ashfield, he realized now that he was not in control of his destiny. He answered the call of his superior officers and tried to do the job that was his duty. If that was a truth, then he had to learn to live with the results.

It was a while coming to him, but a thought emerged as to how he might cope with this. Looking at the slats of the top bunk it came to him. This was all just his opinion—nothing but his opinion of the events. If he thought a thing was bad, then it was so, and if he thought a thing was good, then it was also good. It was just his own damn opinion of whatever was going on around him and to him. If he wanted to change a thing from bad to good, all he had to do was change his opinion of whatever it was.

Simple!

Frank thought about the airman he had seen falling

without his parachute after it had been melted away. That had been a hopeless situation for that man. Then it came to him. If he was falling from an airplane without a parachute there would be no reason to scream and cry— it was all over, and there would be no hope for him. So why not relax and enjoy the view? It would be the last time he would ever get to see it!

It was all just opinion—nothing but his opinion of whatever was happening. So, why not go with the flow? In every situation, there was good and bad, and people simply chose the one they wanted. Why not always pick the good? That's what he would do, he decided. He would change his opinion to select only the good. To hell with the bad!

Frank did not know if he could pull off this mind game he was playing with himself, but it was worth a try. He had constructed a mind tomb for his dead friends and that was constantly giving him problems. He could not keep the cover tight on the tomb and it hurt when the ghostly memories slipped from the tomb and wandered through his dreams—which were really nightmares.

The odds were too great for him to make all of the assigned missions. No way would he live to complete them. He was a dead man and he knew it as he slid the cover back over the opening of his mind tomb.

Alex wanted to go to London to be with Dana and asked Frank to go with him, but Frank declined. He was not good company for anyone, not Alex, not Nichole, not anybody—except maybe Ashly. He was really screwed up. Finally, Alex took off for London without Frank, which was for the best because Frank knew that if he went along he would make everybody miserable.

Frank loaded his .45-caliber sidearm and headed for the base gunnery range. No one else was around so he had it all to himself. Here he would be able to think without interference from anyone, no matter what he did.

Death! It was not all that bad. It would stop all the pain he felt. Who cared if he lived or died? No one gave him a chance to live through all this hell. The good times were just fillers of time until he died. Who gave a damn?

He shot up several hundred rounds of ammo as he thought. He had his own war going on in his head. The nightmares wandered before his mind and he had to rise above his emotions and live up to that expected from him. He was a good soldier and had learned well while in the Army. He would continue to be just that until his time came.

His problems faded into the back of his mind for a time, so he shoved the gun in its holster and headed back to the hut. He was through thinking for a while.

CHAPTER 16

And More Missions

When Alex returned from London, he told Frank that he was going to marry Dana and wanted to know what Frank thought of this. Frank saw how happy Alex seemed and only wanted to know what Dana had to say about it. He did not bring up the dangers of the missions. If it was what they both wanted, then why not? Alex was so elated when Frank agreed that he hugged him.

There was not much time for Alex and Frank to discuss the marriage. On August 9, 1944, they were scheduled for another mission. Frank noted: Tuesday, August 9, D-Day + 64. Target: ME-109 airplane factory at Nuremberg, Germany. Altitude: 24,000 feet. Ten 500-pound bombs. Estimated time of flight: 7 hours. Time on oxygen: 5 hours.

The target was an underground factory that assembled airplanes for the German Air Force. S-2 had information the plant was deep underground and reinforced with heavy concrete structures. It would be protected by many anti-aircraft guns and there would also be many German fighters to deal with. Success in destroying this factory would cut down on the number of fighters the Eighth Air Force would have to face.

The Germans had started a new defense tactic. Instead of scattering guns around lesser important targets, they were placing them all at prime targets such as this factory. Frank had heard that some locations now had more than a thousand anti-aircraft guns and the effect was to down more bombers on every mission.

The mission to the target was not all that bad with only light flak near the cities the Germans thought the group was going to bomb. German fighters did not attack the formation, which was a surprise. When the bomb bay doors opened, this must have been a signal for the anti-aircraft gunners to start firing as the sky became black with smoke from the flak barrage that came up to greet the formation. Several B-17s took hard hits and fell from formation in the first thirty seconds of the bomb run.

The Horse lurched upward as several bursts hit just below Frank's turret. The sound of flak hitting the Horse seemed louder than usual and a piece came into the turret, cutting through Frank's pants leg. His right leg began to feel numb and he was afraid to look at it, thinking he had been hit. He finally removed a glove and without looking down, felt his leg for blood and found none. Shifting to one side, he felt a pain near his groin. Putting his hand there, he felt a parachute harness buckle and moved it to one side. When the buckle moved, he felt a severe tingle in his leg and realized the buckle had cut off his circulation.

The new electrically heated flight suit he had been issued started getting cold and he knew there was a problem with it. Through the turret gun sightglass he saw there was trouble ahead. A squadron of ME-109s was waiting for them to leave the flak area. As the formation of B-17s exited the area, he saw two B-17s trailing behind and below, trying to keep up. One B-17 never had a chance as three ME-109s attacked and made short work of shooting down the airplane. Frank watched it spiraling earthward and then he had a clear opening to fire at one of the ME-109s. He started firing but missed the fighter as it made a pass at the B-17 and cut it to pieces. Frank could only watch helplessly as it burst into flames.

The ME-109s stayed out of gun range and flew forward to join the other fighters forming for an attack from the front of the formation. Frank surveyed the damage under the airplane and was surprised to see such a large hole near his turret. He heard the pilot tell the co-pilot to feather a propeller on an engine that had quit. There was a cold breeze coming through the broken window and his hands and feet were getting numb. He reported the problem to the pilot and was told to stay in the turret, as the German fighters were ready to start an attack.

The ME-109s came head-on into the formation firing 20-mm cannons. A fighter came straight at the Horse and as it went underneath them, not more than a few feet away, Frank saw the German pilot looking up at him, judging position; he looked Frank straight in the eyes. As the fighter flew to the rear, he made the mistake of dropping slightly and that was all Frank needed. He opened fire on the fighter and continued firing until he saw pieces of the airplane stripping off and trailing the ME-109. Frank could not feel his hands or feet and the rest of his body was getting numb. He had to operate the turret controls by sight and thought he could see his tracers hitting the German airplanes, but not many were going down.

Some ME-109s were falling from the sky, shot down

by other gunners on the Horse and in B-17s in upper elements. The fight went on until the P-51s came into view and took on the Germans. The dogfight was left behind as the bombers continued homeward.

It had been over thirty minutes since Frank's suit had lost power and he was nearly frozen. The outside air temperature was 50 degrees below zero and wind was blowing through the shattered window. Frank asked the pilot for permission to leave the turret, since he was freezing. He could no longer feel his hands and feet and his oxygen mask was becoming a chunk of solid ice, making it difficult for him to breathe. Moisture from his breath, which normally condensed and dripped on his neck scarf, had stopped dripping and an icicle had formed.

The pilot radioed for information on the German fighters and was told the formation was in the clear, as the P-51s had taken care of the Germans. The pilot then gave permission for Frank to leave the turret.

Watching where he put his hands and using fingers without feeling, he managed to open the turret door latches and crawl onto the floor of the fuselage. Maneuvering his body, he stood and started to take a step. It was as if he stepped in a hole and fell on the floor of the radio room. He told Don his problem and then just lay there. Don connected the suit to an outlet and brought out an emergency electrically heated hand muff. Don removed Frank's gloves and shoes, then put his hands and feet in the muff. As he regained some feeling in his hands, he began to rub his feet, and after about thirty minutes, he felt a tingling sensation in his feet. He waited a while as he warmed, then had Don help replace his shoes and connect them to the suit legs. Don did the same with his gloves.

After several cigarettes, the two men inspected the turret, discovering that a piece of flak had cut the stem that supported it. The turret was all but cut completely in half and all wiring in the stem had shorted. The wiring seemed to be all that was keeping the turret from falling from the belly of the airplane.

Over the Channel, Alex came to Frank and massaged his arms and lower legs. His hands and feet burned as if they were on fire. At less than 8,000 feet, Frank removed his shoes again and put his feet in the emergency muff.

When they landed, the pilot directed Frank to have the flight line emergency doctor check him. After a brief examination, the doctor said Frank was the luckiest man alive as he had seen men with less frostbite lose their fingers and toes. A ground crewman said the turret should have dropped from the airplane.

Frank, of course, knew what had happened. His personal Guardian Angel had again saved him. No question. It was a fact!

The crew of the Horse was placed on stand-down, as the turret and other damage would take several days to repair and there were no other airplanes for them to fly. Flak damage to the 385th was preventing a lot of airplanes from flying, and spare parts were becoming even harder to find.

Frank asked around to determine if anyone had seen Lieutenant Swartz lately, but the lieutenant was not to be located. Frank guessed he must have been shacking up with his woman, probably staying away from base as much as possible.

It had been a while since Frank had seen Ashly and

he really missed her now that his head was back on straight. The thought of his Princess excited him and gave him reason to live. It was a beautiful afternoon, so he biked along the lane and met her walking on the road. They had a grand reunion as she wept and professed how much she had missed him. He kissed her and the tears stopped as she grabbed and hugged him.

Ashly was alive with joy and could not keep her hands off Frank. He thought she was never going to release him from her grasp. Finally they left the bike and walked the path across a meadow to a rill. She held his hand and danced along the way. The willow trees cast a welcomed shadow over a flat rock that almost dammed the stream.

They could see the ancient mansion in the distance, on top of a rolling hill, and it seemed to be watching over them as they played in the grass. Ashly was vibrant, as he had never before seen her. She removed her shoes and dangled her feet in the cool branch water. Frank went to sit beside her and as he stepped, his foot slipped and into the water he tumbled. He grabbed his cap before it floated away then sat there laughing. Ashly, laughing at the sight of him sitting in the water, waded out and sat beside him. They splashed water on each other for a while and then he asked her why she came in the water.

"I've always heard if you laugh at someone when they have an accident it will happen to you also, so I decided to get it over with, and here I am."

Frank lay back, pulled her atop his chest and held her close as they lay there.

"I hear you were awarded a medal for bravery," she said.

"Yes, how did you find out? Did Swartz tell you?"

"No. Would you believe you are known to more officers than you may think?"

"What do you mean? Known by who?" he asked, as he sat erect looking at her with a questionable expression.

"Aunt Amy told me. She heard it from one of her friends when she asked about you."

"So it wasn't Swartz. I've not seen him lately and wondered what's happened to him. You seen him lately?"

"No. Now that I think of it, I have not seen him here in more than a week."

"What about his lady friend, has she left? Maybe they eloped." Frank laughed at the thought.

"She's still here but you should see her. Large, really large with child. She must have been that way for a long while. I feel so sorry for the woman."

"I don't want to see her. I want only to see you."

The two of them played, splashing water on each other, and he gently rolled her in the cool water until both were thoroughly soaked. Finally he stood, removed his clothing, waded to the bank, and placed the clothing on a rock to dry. Ashly watched as if it were the greatest performance she had ever witnessed.

Frank sat on the rock and watched as she removed her clothes and handed them to him to place with his. He thought his Princess was the most beautiful female he had ever seen as he lay back on the rock and drank in her beauty. Never had he thought anyone so beautiful would ever give him a second glance.

Frank was lying back on the warm rock when Ashly came to him. The smooth, sunshine-heated rock felt good to his bare backside, as did her cool firm breasts on his chest as she accepted him. He had not seen her so active and carefree before and enjoyed the fact she wanted him just as he was. Other girls he had been with before entering the service were prudish and afraid of what someone would say about them, always wanting to be so secretive about their flings with boys. Here they were out in the middle of nowhere, and Ashly seemed not to care who might see them.

They rolled onto the soft moss growing on the rocks where the sun never fully shone. They lay there resting, her never far from him, always with her hands on his body, as if she were afraid he would disappear from her reach.

Frank thought he would like to be with her forever but it seemed that would not be. As close as they had become, he did not really know much about her. He wanted to ask about her life but was afraid he might spoil their relationship. Besides, what did he have to offer other than a few days of his life? He decided not to ask now, thinking his Guardian Angel would have to lead him to find out more at the proper time.

After resting and warming in the sun, they played in the stream until the day was waning. Their clothes had not dried well and the sun was setting, creating a beautiful sight as the red ball and the scattered clouds painted the sky with such beautiful colors of blue, pink and gold.

"I don't know what your aunt is going to say when she sees us. I guess we may as well find out. Let's dress and go get our *you know what*'s chewed out."

"You have been in the army too long. She is not going to be like one of your officers. You'll see."

Deciding he would have no way out of this one, they dressed and headed for the mansion.

"What in heavens name happened to the two of you?" her aunt asked. "You both look just like when I last saw Frank and he was soaked to the skin. What happened?"

Ashly told about Frank falling into the water and how she, too, had become wet. Then the three of them had a good laugh about it.

"Aunt Amy, please send Charles for our clothes to take care of them."

"Run along. Charles is busy but will be there in a short while. You two look like wet chickens."

Frank had finished his bath with Ashly and was sharing the towel with her when they heard a knock on the door.

"Miss Ashly, Sergeant Mays, I came for the clothes," Charles said as he opened the door.

Frank grabbed one of Ashly's robes, tried to tie the waist belt, and went to the door. As the door came full open, so did the robe, which had come untied, exposing Frank to Charles. He was expecting the butler to laugh aloud, but without as much as a grin, Charles picked up their clothes and turned to leave.

"I will have these back in one hour, Sergeant Mays."

The hour passed quickly—too quickly for Frank, as he and Ashly were not dressed when Charles returned with the clothes. Ashly made him wait as she put on the robe Frank had worn when Charles came for the clothes. Frank wondered what he thought, but then remembered where he was and imagined that Charles was beyond the point of being shocked in this house. The clothes had been dried, pressed, folded and placed on racks.

Frank enjoyed seeing Ashly dress as much he did watching her undress. This was a totally new experience for him. He was pleased when she asked him to fasten her bra, knowing that she didn't really need his help. He was probably more of a hindrance than he was a help, anyway, and questioned why she put up with his foolishness the way she did. Then he decided it was probably best if he didn't know.

Having finally finishing dressing, Ashly uncovered the painting and the figure before Frank suggested more arms and legs than necessary. She must have been painting in some temporary changes and had not completed the work. Still, it was the work of a master artist.

"You see me as a spider or is that an octopus?"

"Neither. I'm searching for the best pose and have not yet come to a decision. Once chosen, it will take me but a short while to make a finished portrait."

"Thank God! For a moment I thought you saw me as some sort of monster."

"You are my monster and I love you for being just that. I believe there is another full moon tonight. Will you pose for me for a while? The moonlight gives you a glow that I want to capture on the canvas."

"Why don't we open the French doors and let the moon shine in the room," Frank suggested. "Or if you choose, you can work and we'll sleep on the balcony. I like to watch you sleep."

"I do not mean sleep. I want to paint and we can sleep wherever you choose. You may be correct, just inside the door would give the correct effect I want. I must work on the portrait and finish it soon. I'll have Charles bring us sandwiches and tea later. Will that please you, my Master?"

"Sounds fine to me. The night air is warm and there's no breeze stirring. I'm with you, what more could I want other than to please you?"

As Ashly prepared for painting, Frank walked on the balcony and looked over the estate. The moon was rising, a full orange ball on the horizon. It reminded him of the sunset they had observed earlier, just in the negative view. He did not mention it to Ashly, but as he walked back through the French doors, he thought he saw the same ghostly figure he had spotted on her balcony that first night. He thought maybe all these old places had ghosts, or perhaps he was just remembering stories he had read in school.

The moonlight was just what Ashly wanted and she slaved on the portrait with Frank posing at her whims. She covered her work each time she rested and he never saw the work in progress. It was in the early morning hours when Ashly put away her brushes. They were both tired and went straight to sleep as soon as they lay down on her soft bed.

The following morning, after bathing and dressing, they ate a full breakfast in the kitchen with Aunt Amy. The food was nothing like the greasy stuff he got on base, but still he became nauseated after eating. He did not lose the food but sure wished he could have.

Ashly then led him through some of the secret passages and into small hidden rooms where he saw clutter of old military equipment that must have been centuries old. Frank played with a sword, but it made Ashly nervous so he stopped. She then led him out into the formal garden to the spot where the officers had seen them running about that first night. As they sat on one of the benches, Frank decided he had to ask some questions of his Princess.

"Ashly, I want to ask something and please don't get mad. If you don't want to answer it will be okay, just let me know and I'll stop. Okay?"

She put her arms around him and smiled as she nodded for him to continue.

"You told me that Aunt Amy asked about me at the base so you have some idea who I am. Will you tell me anything about yourself?"

"Like you, I am of Scottish blood, and I wanted that in the man I met. No other suited my picture of my ideal person as well as you. Other than that, I would like to drop the subject. Maybe we'll talk some other time."

With that as an answer, Frank decided not to push the matter further at this time, and he changed the subject. Their being of similar Scottish backgrounds made him feel even closer to Ashly.

CHAPTER 17

Happy Birthday

Frank had several more questions he wanted to ask Ashly, but the opportunity never arose, as he became engrossed in her requests for him to pose. He was having a good time while Ashly had him pose in different positions as she painted. He would clown around and at times he became aroused, so it was not all work, as she had to stop and partake of his offerings. They took a break and walked in the moonlight through the garden to the rill, where they fooled around for a while. When they returned, Ashly worked as if possessed to finish the painting.

When it came time for Frank to leave, Ashly dressed in some of her finest clothing. She looked so beautiful, so radiant and so alive, as if she really were his Princess.

Sunday, August 13, 1944, Mission number 26, D-Day + 68.

HAPPY BIRTHDAY TO FRANK! He was twenty years old today ... How about that! He was flying his 26th mission on his 20th birthday. He had made it to twenty and this mission would put him over the top. Just maybe he could make all those missions after all. He never mentioned his birthday to anyone, although he wished he had told Ashly and wondered why he hadn't.

The target for today was a bridge in the Seine area

and they would hit it from low altitude. It should be a true *milk run*. It would be a 6-1/2 hour flight and not on oxygen, all in an area where they could support the ground troops.

"My Guardian Angel has worked a small miracle," he thought as he climbed in the waist door of the Horse. He had lost his breakfast again but that didn't dampen his spirit. Still, he wished I could stop this throwing up every morning, he thought as the Horse left the runway.

The ground troops were making a breakthrough and they wanted to bottle-up the Germans for a mass surrender. The bridges over the river allowed German vehicles to retreat and the Americans wanted them stopped so they could capture or destroy German equipment. This would cripple the Germans and the low-level bombers would have a field day destroying equipment.

As the formation of B-17 bombers left the English coast to cross the Channel, Frank noted the time: 6:45 a.m., the exact time he had been born, twenty years ago. What a wonderful day this would be for old Frank Mays. He would no longer be a teenager. Of course, he was far beyond that age in experience. The world had been good to him, with some crap along the way, but not all that bad. He had made true friends, something that before the war he had not known existed.

The group of airplanes was at 14,000 feet as they crossed into France and the sky was clear and deep blue in all directions. Below the Horse, Frank could see the land the briefing officer had described, and as he had predicted, there was no flak because they were over friendly troops. He could see the troops on the move as the airplane dropped to 8,000 feet. Many American tanks were going in the same direction, weaving through the hedgerows and the foot troops would be following the paths cleared by the tanks.

The formation of bombers split into 11 elements of three airplanes each and headed for their previously selected targets. The Horse's target was a bridge over a small river. Their three-plane element descended to 4,000 feet and dropped thirty-eight 100-pound bombs on the bridge—one bridge no longer there for the Germans to use.

The airplanes received some small cannon fire on the bomb run but none hit the Horse. The element then climbed back to 14,000 feet, reassembled with the other 32 airplanes and headed back to Great Ashfield. All planes returned safely to base. A true *milk run*. What a way to celebrate a birthday! Thanks, Guardian Angel!

At the mess hall, Frank received his ration of grog and drank it down with pleasure, but the greasy food just did not set right on his stomach. There had to be some reason for the upset stomach and he tried to think what it might be.

On missions like the one to Nuremberg where German fighters hit, he felt different from when there was only flak. He realized the fighters gave him an opportunity to fight back whereas with the flak he just had to sit there and take his chances. It could be nothing more than a nervous stomach. He had heard about morning sickness when men's wives became pregnant but discounted that because he knew that one of his girlfriends did not have a problem. He wasn't so sure about Ashly. No way did he want to get a girl pregnant, only to be shot down on one of his last missions. Besides that, this just did not seem like a nice world in which to bring a new life.: And after the way his father had raised him, Frank wasn't sure he ever wanted to have children. He was afraid they might react toward him as he had toward his father. No, this world now was not a nice place for children to be raised what with all the killing.

Leaving the mess hall, Frank went to his hut and along the way he inquired about the whereabouts of Lieutenant Swartz. None of the airmen had seen Swartz so Frank would have to go higher to satisfy his curiosity. He went to see the First Sergeant and in their casual conversation, he slipped in some questions about officers.

Boom! As soon as Frank mentioned Swartz, the sergeant dropped a bomb! Swartz was no longer a member of the 385th Bomb Group. The sergeant proceeded to tell Frank that the Brass had discovered some information about Swartz that resulted in the transfer, if it could be called a transfer. The sergeant was not privy to the entire story but Swartz had been sent from the base because of something big. The story was under wraps and no one was talking.

Rumor had it that Swartz was in trouble because of some connection with a British women. Some of the officers knew he had money problems, but the way he was trying to solve these must have gotten him in big trouble with S-2. Frank wondered if Swartz was connected with the spy ring and had been exchanging information for cash.

In any case, Frank kissed his money goodbye. He was overjoyed that Swartz was gone, though. Now there would be no way for anyone to connect him to fraternizing with an officer. He guessed it had been a fair trade, as his meeting Ashly in the deal made it all right.

The sergeant added, "Some of the officers brought up your name in connection with Swartz but they said you were a fine soldier."

Could Swartz or one of the women be a spy? What was going on at that brothel other than hanky panky? He had not seen anything to suggest this, but a spy would be sneaky. All Frank cared about there was his Princess. He had been exposed to some of the Brass at the brothel but he didn't know them and thought they would not remember him. Of course, since he was the only enlisted man who went there, he must have stood out like a sore thumb. Were they afraid he could tell tales and that was why they labeled him a fine soldier? Better yet, perhaps Aunt Amy had them all by the balls. Could she have had a hand in saving his ass? That must be what happened, he decided.

Except for that first time when he went to the brothel with Swartz, Frank had spoken to the lieutenant only in passing. Of course, someone could have spotted him there any of a number of times. He had done nothing wrong, except for the time the two officers saw Ashly and him playing nude in the garden and messing around. He remembered they had called out, "Hey Sergeant," and scared the crap out of him. They had to know him to have used the word "Sergeant," so they must have seen him there before.

Frank had to laugh when he thought about how they had given the old boys a show for their money. Maybe he had shown them something to prove that he was a fine soldier. "Frank, old boy, you're gonna have to keep your clothes on and stop showing up those officers."

Alex wanted to know what was so damned funny when Frank walked in the hut door, but he just said he'd heard a dirty joke a while ago and it had just struck him funny. He hated lying to Alex but thought it best. He would explain it to Alex later and he would understand. He did not want to involve Alex in this matter in the event something came of the situation. Frank quit laughing, went to his bunk and stretched out to think.

Alex probably knew that he had been lied to, but he was too good a friend to push Frank. Finally, Alex asked Frank to go with him to the recreation hall and get a cup of tea. They were beginning to like the taste of the British drink, even without sugar.

Frank hung around the base all day listening for any word that might implicate him in something other than screwing around over at the brothel. He was paying attention to how the officers reacted to him. Most of them were straight and did not gamble or fool around with women. Many had wives back in the States and were true blue to them. Frank began to think he was a bit paranoid, as he could have sworn some of the officers grinned as he walked past. He did recognize several men that he had observed through the peepholes, but they appeared now as if they didn't care who he was. It had to be one of Dame Metcalf's close friends; otherwise, he was sure the Army would have his ass.

"So much for being a private eye," he thought.

"Why in hell are you watching all these officers?" Alex asked. "You're sure not yourself today, Frank."

"Alex, did you ever know something you were afraid to tell because it might get somebody in trouble?"

"Yeah, I guess so. You know something you think you can't tell me?"

"That's what I've been thinking, but I've changed my pea-sized brain. I really feel bad for not having told you before and if I can't trust you, then I'm in deep shit."

Frank walked Alex away from the hut and made sure no one could overhear, then laid the entire story on him: Swartz, the brothel, the money Swartz borrowed and what the First Sergeant had said about him being a fine soldier. He went into detail about his suspicion that Swartz could be a spy. Of course, that was a long shot, but it had to be considered.

"I don't see where you have a problem, Frank. Looks like somebody likes you and is willing to give you a break. From what you say, it could be the Dame or any one of the officers that go there. Just thank your lucky stars."

Both men became quiet and kept watch for any sign that an officer was paying particular attention to Frank.

Lucky stars? Better yet, his Guardian Angel, Frank thought as he let his mind bring forth memories later while listening to the small radio in the hut. The song now playing was "That Old Black Magic." When that tune finished, "Always" came from the radio, which stayed tuned to the station where a young woman named Axis Sally in Berlin played all the soldiers' favorite songs. Of course, she dropped in her digs of propaganda but the men laughed at her attempts to demoralize them.

Lucky? He remembered when he had arrived at Camp Lee in Virginia just after being drafted. Among the examinations had been that IQ test and it had blown the tester's mind when Frank came up with a score of 160—twice. That country boy should never have scored so high but it didn't mean beans. He was later to find out it was a test of intelligence and not knowledge. He was like an empty bucket and the Army proceeded to fill that void with ways to kill people. With a high school diploma, his military career might have been quite different, but still, he was satisfied with his life. Life was good to him. Except for a sore heel and knee, he was in good shape—good enough to get some pretty girls and that wasn't bad for a country boy.

When he had received basic training in Miami, Florida, his drill instructor, an Army veteran of fifteen years, had taken a liking to Frank and crushed him with all his knowledge, never letting up. He was Frank's mentor and tried to teach him everything about the Army in just eight weeks. It had been difficult to follow all the military knowledge poured upon him, but he learned it well. When basic training was completed, the drill instructor tried to have the Brass take Frank in as an instructor, but Frank wanted no part of that job. He wanted action and it seemed he had gotten just what he wished.

Frank had been sent from Miami to Gulfport, Mississippi for airplane mechanic training, where he completed the five-month course rated top in his class. The schooling taught Frank just about all there was to know about the B-17 Flying Fortress. He soaked up information in the classrooms, tech manuals and actual work on the airplane. As the ball turret was of special interest to him, he learned its functions and mechanical systems as well or better than the instructors did. He was given hands-on training in the field and again was asked to stay on as an instructor. Once more, he refused a stateside job.

There were only two personal memories that stood out in his mind from Gulfport. One was that buck sergeant named Scully, who tried but could find nothing with which to demerit Frank, so he just plain harassed him. Frank swore that one day he would rank with Scully and then he would look him up and whip his ass.

The other thing was when he and Bob went to the Edgewater Beach Hotel and stayed the night with the girls. They had sneaked the airmen into their rooms where Frank and his girl pretended that she was Scarlet and he was Rhett Butler at Tara. He remembered the décor of the room being good old southern antebellum.

Then he remembered the troop train stops in Abilene, Texas. He would never forget that female marine officer. She was something else. He wondered if she became pregnant and got her medical discharge from the Corps, as she must have wanted. That lieutenant sure knew what she wanted, and he had done his best to help a marine the best way he knew how.

Lucky? No question about it. He had certainly made friends, and how about all those combat missions? So far, all he had to show for them was a low back pain and a bruise on his left heel. He looked now and saw that the bruise was still the color of moldy grape jelly. His back and neck hurt at times and his knee and heel were still sore. He wondered if the flak had broken a heel or anklebone. He had stuck his neck out by fraternizing with an officer. Maybe that was why it hurt. However, that was a case of an officer suckering him into a deal in which he had no other choice. Of course, meeting Ashly made it worth all the pain.

Yes, somebody was looking out for him, so why not a Guardian Angel? He sure was not an agnostic because every man that stuck his ass in a ball turret had to believe in something. He'd heard that the life of a ball turret gunner in combat averaged about twelve minutes. He had over 200 hours and that made his odds about 1000 to 1. Yeah, he had a Guardian Angel, no question about that.

He had made his peace with his God and accepted that he would be killed. He only prayed to have it be quickly, not like the guy who walked through the spinning propeller, and not like Lieutenant Butt and the slow painful agony he had suffered. Frank wished he could have done more for the lieutenant but it just was not within his power. The man had been hurt too severely for anyone to save him.

The blood of two friends had covered his skin and stained his flight suit. The stains were still visible as dark areas and Supply had tried to issue him a new suit, but he would have no part of that. He cherished the fact that *they* were still with him on every mission. Besides his memories, the stains were all he had by which to remember his friends. Most men carried some good-luck charm with them on every mission and he wore his with pride.

Superstition? Maybe yes, maybe no—probably yes! One day they would all be together again, and maybe even in the same flight suit.

The radio music played on.

Who else but Alex could snap this morbid state of mind? "Get your ass up and let's go guzzle a beer."

Frank grinned at the sound of Alex's voice. He

bounded from his bunk and caught Alex by surprise with his back to him. He wrapped both arms around his friend, lifted him from the floor, dropped him and hit him on the arm with his fist.

"What the hell was that all about?"

"You don't really want to know. Let's go see if we can find that beer. I'm paying."

"I don't know if I want to drink with you. You could hurt a fellow." Alex rubbed his arm as he laughed.

Walking down toward the squadron entrance, Frank put an arm around Alex. He felt good after remembering all the good things in his life and Alex was one of them. With a silly cocked eye, Alex looked at Frank and said, "Don't you think people will talk, seeing us like this?"

Frank laughed. "Who gives a shit? I don't, do you?"

"Nope!"

Alex put an arm around Frank. They couldn't care less what anyone thought, as they were the best of friends. Besides that, they would whip anyone's ass that said anything.

One beer, that's all they had over a long period. In fact, the beer went flat while they were talking. This was just a pastime, a chance to talk.

"Have you and Dana set a date yet? Thought it would've been before now."

"What are you talking about? I don't know what you mean," Alex replied with a big grin on his face.

"Asshole, I'm sure glad for you. I'll bet it's the paperwork, right?"

There was lots of conversation concerning Dana, Nichole and Ashly. They finally threw away the flat beers, as it was time to check the bulletin board. Alex and

Frank stopped by the latrine and disposed of the beer then headed for the squadron area. The 10:30 loading list had been posted and the crew of the Horse was to fly the next morning, so it was off to the sack.

CHAPTER 18

Back in the Saddle

Tuesday, August 15, 1944, Mission number 27, D-Day + 70. Target: Airfield. Location: Handorf, Germany. This mission was to take out a German airfield and was the type of mission Frank liked. Any time they could get the bastards on the ground and ruin their nesting place it was good for all aircrews.

Frank's group had not been seeing as many fighters lately as some of the other groups that were getting their tails shot off. It was reported fighters were hitting one particular group every time they went out. The talk among the airmen was that the men of the 100th Bomb Group were the ones taking all the beating. It seemed an airplane from that group was badly damaged by flak on a particular mission. When the German fighters came to shoot down the airplane, the Americans dropped their wheels as a sign of surrender and the fighters pulled beside the airplane to escort it to a German airfield. When the bomber pilot discovered that his airplane was not as badly damaged as he had thought, he gave orders to fire on the German fighters. The Germans, unaware of the decision, had let down their guard, and as the waist gunners opened fire, they shot down the two fighters.

Since the 100th Bomb Group had violated a code of war, the Germans decided they would not let the Americans get away with the act and for revenge, they began to leave other bombers in the heat of battle and attack the airplanes of the 100th Bomb Group. Whenever the 100th was in the area, all German fighters relished shooting down their bombers, which caused the loss of several of the 100th Group's airplanes.

The night after the mission to Handorf, the crew of the Horse found their names on the list to fly again the next day. The crew and aircraft were in good shape and were needed, as many planes had been damaged over Handorf.

Wednesday, August 16, 1944, Mission number 28, D-Day + 71.

This was a long flight to Rositz, Germany, located somewhere near Leipzig. The target, a German oil dump, was vital to the vehicles that were attacking Allied forces. The best way to slow the Germans was to stop their supply of fuel, and fuel depots had become critical targets. The attacks on the fuel dumps seemed to be working, as the Air Corps had not been seeing as many German fighters as before.

As the formation approached the IP, the pilot turned over controls to the bombardier, but when he opened the bomb bay doors, a first class malfunction occurred. The bombs salvoed out of the bomb bay while the Horse was still two miles from the target. Frank could do nothing but sit there and watch as ten 500-pound bombs fell on what appeared to be a wheat field. He thought, "If we can't kill them we'll starve them to death." Frank imagined that some German farmer would curse them for destroying his crop. The Horse still had to stay in formation, flying through all the hellish flak, taking hits and trying to stay alive without any bombs to drop.

Luckily, no one was injured.

Later they found that a piece of flak had shorted the wiring in the bomb bay causing the malfunction. When the bombardier pushed the button to open the bomb bay doors, it had also released the bombs. The doors would not close and had to be hand-cranked shut.

Friday, August 18, 1944, Mission number 29, D-Day + 73. Estimated length of mission: 8 hours.

The target was an airfield located near Paris and the crew of the Horse disliked going anywhere near there, as the death of Lieutenant Butt still hung in all their minds, especially Frank's. To the enjoyment of the crew, the mission turned out to be a true *milk run*. No German fighters appeared, and there was only light flak. The field at St. Dizier was destroyed as Frank watched the bombs plow through buildings and runways, leaving nothing but fire and plumes of smoke from the fuel tanks.

Something happened during the next several days that really stuck in the craw of the airmen. From command and from the military newspaper, the airmen learned that a number of unions back in the States were out on strike. This soon began affecting all military operations around the world as badly needed supplies, including gas and bombs, were arriving more slowly.

The men were told that President Roosevelt would have to intervene to force the strikers back to work. Coal mines in Pennsylvania were shut down and not a lump of coal from that state was available for the war effort. Many items that had once been rationed at the PX were now just not available at all.

The squadron commander allowed the men

passes to leave the base and Alex took off for London. Frank knew that Alex was head over heels in love with Dana and decided it best if he went alone. Besides that, Frank wanted to visit Ashly. He missed her and knew he was pushing his luck with 29 missions under his belt.

Ashly and Frank reviewed the portrait and he was glad to see that he no longer had too many arms and legs. "I like what I see now," he told her. "The coloring seems to have changed and it looks more mystical—not just so much like a naked man standing there. Now that's art."

She smiled. "I'm so glad you approve. It's most important to me. I still see some changes I need to make, though. Do you have a pass so you can stay a while?"

"The entire base is on stand-down for the next several days. I think I can stay as long as you want me. I also have some news that you probably already know but I still want to talk to you about it."

"I assume you mean about Lieutenant Swartz. Yes, I heard about that and we should talk."

The two lovers walked in the flower garden and when they came to their favorite seat, they sat and the maid brought tea sent by Aunt Amy.

Frank thought, "She doesn't miss a trick. Aunt Amy knows everything that goes on around here. Guess it's her business to keep track of everyone, including me."

Finishing the tea, they left the tray on the bench and walked to the rill. The flat rock with the soft moss was a favorite spot of Ashly's. She commented, "I will have to construct a monument at this place. I'll always remember the day we first played in the water. I can see your face and hear that hardy laugh of yours as you sat in the middle of the stream with your clothes on."

Frank laughed and said, "Yeah, I'll remember that day as well. I had never seen a water nymph before."

The mid-August weather was hotter than normal for England. Frank remembered that were it not for the gulf stream flowing south near Ireland all this land would be cold, even in the summertime. Where they were standing was about 52 degrees north of the equator and that was far north of Gander, Newfoundland, where they had landed when he flew over from the States. There had been four feet of snow on the ground in May, with more on the way. He wondered if the snow ever melted and why people chose to live in places like that.

As Frank lay on his bare stomach in the soft moss, Ashly massaged his back. Her fingers worked like magic to loosen his taut muscles. She had already relaxed his mind and he was enjoying the extra attention. From where he lay, the sight of the mansion reminded him of the place in Scotland where he'd spent his first night in this foreign land. Frank's ancestors had emigrated from Scotland and landed in the New World at Jamestown in 1628. He remembered seeing a Scottish girl that first night in Scotland, and that she looked a lot like Ashly, but he could not remember for sure, as he had been so excited back then. That young girl had come from the large house on the hill to visit and greet the arriving airmen. He remembered the beautiful dress she wore, which might have been just like the one Ashly wore when they first met.

All these old places were reported to have ghosts and tales were told about them. He and Ashly had added to the store of memories for this mansion and may have shocked some of its ghosts. He remembered seeing what might have been the ghost of Richard, whoever he might be.

"You seem to be lost in your own dream world," Ashly said.

"Sorry, I was just daydreaming."

"And I thought I was your dream."

How would he tell her of his rambling thoughts? Simple, just stay with the truth, he decided. "I was thinking of how you and I may have shocked this old house with our gallivanting around the house and yards."

"I'm sure they could teach us a thing or two from what I've heard about the history of this place. And what is going on in the other side, what could we learn from them? Let's go look at history being made. I want to check on the Karros woman, anyway. She's been very ill lately and I heard she may lose her baby."

"Before we go, tell me one thing. Did Swartz come here to care for the woman before he left for parts unknown?"

"Oh, no! Aunt Amy would shoot him if he ever showed up here again. He tried to involve you in some nasty business in conversations with other officers here, but Aunt Amy put a stop to that. The men are her card buddies and after she told them about you and me, why they decided that you're a fine soldier."

Frank thought, "Where have I heard that statement before? Yep, it was just as I thought—Aunt Amy."

In Ashly's room, the conversation continued about the old house and that was when Ashly recounted a tale that he would never forget.

"When Aunt Amy was my age she fell in love with a

young man in her art class. Since they had the same art teacher for so many years, their paintings looked almost the same. Just as I am painting you, they did something similar. It even took place here in this very room. They were very much in love and tried to show it in the type portraits they painted. You—we—remind me so much of the story she told after that. Lay your head in my lap as I finish the story."

She sat looking out over the balcony with a dreamy look upon her face and Frank stretched out with his head in her lap and listened.

"There was one difference. Aunt Amy painted her beau in the buff and on the same canvas where he painted her. The painting has figures slightly smaller than this one of you. It still hangs downstairs and you have seen where, but you didn't know it. A large drapery covers the portraits and only a few people have ever seen them. It's like a guarded treasure. You probably thought there was a window behind that closed drape." She paused for a moment and smiled.

"I probably should've started at another beginning, but I'll continue from here. Shortly after the portrait was completed, her beau entered the military. That was in 1917. He had been in the military only three months when he was killed. Aunt Amy never recovered from the crushing blow of his death. About that time, she inherited this place from her family and she could not bring herself to leave. She never married but loved to see other people happy. A few years after she received word of his death, she decided to take in boarders. It was much later when she got this wild idea to make the place into a brothel. This has been her life ever since—

not a nice one, perhaps, but she is happy. My family lets me spend time here with her for a special reason, one I cannot discuss with anyone. Please forgive me now and maybe one day I will be allowed to tell you. Just yesterday, I let her see the painting of you and when she left the room, I heard her crying outside on the stairwell. I went to console her and she took me to view the painting downstairs. I could see in her eyes there was something she wanted to tell me. As we viewed the portrait, she pointed out how much you and her Richard look alike."

Ashly looked down at him and smiled.

"Yes, two handsome men so much alike. I have looked at the portrait and wished for a man just like him. I have had my wish come true. I will never forget the first time I saw you. I hardly believed my eyes. In fact, the two of you could be twin brothers. He also was of Scottish descent just like you. It's as if you were clan members. Oh, I probably should not have said that. She might show you the painting someday. Now, what do you think of all that?"

When Ashly had said *twin brother*, Frank could not help but remember what Nichole had said about her Alfred. So that was the Richard he had seen on the balcony! Her Richard had never forgotten his Amy. The story explained why Aunt Amy liked him, but opened many questions he dared not ask. Amy had had to face the officers, but how much had she told them? Did they know the story he had just heard? Had his dangerous job of flying come into the picture of why he had been selected to meet Ashly? Could it have been Ashly that he saw that first night in Scotland? Had there been a plan all along for the two of them to meet? With all the young airmen coming through that place in Scotland, why me, he wondered? There was so much for him to consider.

"You look stunned. Are you all right?" asked Ashly.

"I'd only been kidding when I spoke of this place having ghosts, but this is something else. Yes, it did stun me."

"Let's sit here and enjoy the setting sun. It's always so beautiful this time of year."

From her balcony, they looked over the garden at the trees casting their long dark shadows. The deep green contrasted with the rose-colored wispy clouds and reddening sky. Frank thought he felt Richard's presence nearby and wondered if he was waiting for Frank to join him on one of his missions. There was that possibility, as his luck could run out any day. Or was it possible that Richard just liked watching Ashly and him enjoying this room? He had beaten all the odds and if it were not for his Guardian Angel, he would have gone before now. He remembered to thank his Angel.

Frank thought it odd that Aunt Amy never mentioned anything to him concerning what went on in the other side of the mansion. Never a word or a hint of an invitation did he hear from her. Maybe she didn't want him involved with any girls other than Ashly, which was fine with Frank.

Later as the three of them sat in the kitchen, it seemed as if Aunt Amy was bursting to be in their conversation. Ashly had done most all the talking, with Frank saying very little.

"Ashly, have you shown Frank around the house? I want him to see the Grand Hall before he leaves today."

"Yes, Aunt Amy, we toured last night and viewed most of the place. We also visited the servants' quarters and stables so he could see the carriages that you no longer use."

"Yes, those were the days of grandeur, when I dressed up and rode in the horse-drawn carriages. I miss all that."

They continued with small talk until they finished their tea, and then Frank told them he would have to return to base in the afternoon in case his name was listed for a mission. The rest of the day they spent outside in the garden and down at the flat rock.

It was getting late when Frank biked back to base. He found that Alex had returned from London and was on a nonstop talking spree about Dana. There was no one else in the world now but her, except for Frank, who was the perfect listener. He enjoyed seeing how happy his buddy was and it was great to see the brightness on Alex's face. Finally, Alex asked Frank about Ashly, and seemed glad to hear Frank's description of how much they loved each other.

Frank did not mention his questions concerning why he and Ashly were set-up to meet. Alex would brush off his ideas that there was more to this meeting than met the eye. He would probably say, "Frank, don't look a gift-horse in the mouth."

The next morning found the Horse in a formation of B-17s heading out over the English Channel. Frank had made notes on his paper that this mission was to Berlin. Over the Channel, before reaching the German coast, the number 3 engine started streaming oil back under the wing. As Frank was reporting the leak to the pilot, an oil cooler ruptured and oil poured from the engine. The pilots immediately cut the engine and feathered the propeller.

When the pilot notified the formation commander, the Horse was ordered to leave the group and return to base, which was normal procedure for an airplane having problems before reaching enemy territory. There was no need to make a crew fly to a target, especially Berlin, with already a problem before going in.

Frank was glad the mission was aborted, since all the American airplanes were badly damaged every time on Berlin raids. He corrected his notes to read: August 27, 1944. Mission number ? No credit. D-Day + 82. Spare parts to repair the engine were difficult to find and the crew was placed on stand-down.

Frank still could not get Swartz off his mind, as the officer had placed him in a position to get busted. There were many rumors about the man but nothing concrete.

Frank intended to visit Ashly, but Alex secured two London passes for a trip off base and he talked Frank him into going with him, so at 4:05 p.m., they headed for London. Frank rationalized that Nichole could be fun, too, but realized that Ashly should have come first.

CHAPTER 19

Buzz Bombs

The streets of London were almost clear of both British and American soldiers. Even the American Bar, their first stop, was almost empty. Not seeing anyone they knew, Alex and Frank left for the Greek restaurant. Nichole was there and Alex left to locate Dana.

Nichole and Frank went to a theater across from Hyde Park to view a film she wanted to see. There were only a few people in the theater and when the air raid alarm went off, there was no stampede to leave the place. The local people scurried to shelters but Frank stopped as he saw streaks of fire in the night sky, creating a sight unlike any that he had ever before seen. Searchlights were playing on what appeared to be short, stubby airplanes. Anti-aircraft guns located on the far side of the park were firing at the objects.

The two stared at the sight as shells burst overhead. The sound these objects made was a loud roar such as a large truck might make when pulling a steep grade. They moved back underneath the cover of the theater entryway as shrapnel began falling around them. Moments later, the roaring stopped and loud explosions were heard.

Later, Frank was to learn that he had experienced one of the first V-1 or *Buzz Bomb* attacks on London. So that was the secret weapon they had bombed near Paris.

When the all-clear siren sounded, Frank walked with

Nichole over into Hyde Park and people reappeared as life went on in a normal manner. As they walked, he thought about how these people had gotten used to this way of life after years of the Germans bombing them every night. He wondered how the people back home would have handled a similar situation.

It was a warm summer night and they spent most of the evening in Hyde Park. The orators returned to their boxes and people gathered to listen and heckle the speakers. The park began to fill with young girls and Nichole quickly decided to leave after several tried to put the make on Frank.

He remembered not having seen any youngsters under the age of sixteen anywhere in the city and asked Nichole where all the young children were. She told him they were sent to live in the country when Hitler began bombing the cities four years ago.

For the next few hours, they stayed at Nichole's flat, with her making sure Frank did not have reason to stray. With the heavy blackout drapes fully drawn and no electric fan, the room was sweltering. The Lifebuoy soap was put to an extreme test that night as he enjoyed being with his Greek Goddess. He thought Apollo, his namesake, would have been proud of him that night.

The following morning, Dana and Alex came by to go to her cheese and toast restaurant. Frank ate toast but could not handle the baked beans they offered because his stomach was still just not right when it came to breakfast food.

Alex was aglow as he took Frank aside and told him that Dana was pregnant. He seemed so happy as he told Frank they had decided they wanted him to be the godfather. The wedding plans would have to be rushed now, but Alex made Frank promise not to tell the other crewmen. Frank couldn't have been happier for his buddy.

CHAPTER 20

Downtime

On September 1, the Horse and crew flew another mission to Caen, France to remove some beach guns, which were keeping the invasion troops from advancing on that front. It turned out to be another *milk run* and no one was injured nor did the Horse sustain damage.

The next day, September 2, they bombed Brest to rout the Germans. This was almost 90 days after the troops had landed on the Normandy beach on D-Day. No German fighters showed up but the flak was dense. The Germans rallied to hold these areas, but the bombing allowed the troops to advance and capture the towns and this breakthrough started a deep move into France.

Frank now had 30 missions to his credit, and was looking at five more to complete his tour of duty. The military newspaper "Stars and Stripes" had been full of news concerning the labor strikes back in the States, and this news really angered the airmen of the 385th. Here they were getting their asses shot off for about a hundred bucks a month and the strikers wanted *better working conditions* and a pay raise. The men of the Air Corps vowed they would trade places with the 4F bastards any day, even at less pay.

Part of the news concerned a major auto manufacturer that was on strike, which slowed production of needed military vehicles. The airmen were fighting mad at the people back home. No one could understand how the Americans were willing to jeopardize the troops for a little money. It was not just in England, but troops all around the world. Steel mills were on a slowdown and wildcat strikes broke out across the country. Ships needed coal to operate so they were locked in port. All supplies to the troops were still being rationed, including gas and bombs.

It finally caught up with them, as there were no bombs or gas for the airplanes. The Stateside strikes and German U-boats now kept the Air Corps grounded except for the most critical flights. The last news received was that President Roosevelt had ordered John L. Lewis to reopen ten coal mines in Pennsylvania on August 31, but supplies would still be weeks behind schedule.

It seemed as if the unions selected the summer of 1944 to force management of industries to renew contracts that had been hanging since 1943, and screw the troops overseas. Many ground troops died because of the actions of these unions. The soldiers considered that the people back home were letting them down and resented the actions of the strikers.

Mark, King, Alex and Frank received passes and visited a small village fifty miles south of Great Ashfield. Once there, Alex changed his mind and went on to London to see Dana. Frank knew they were making final wedding plans. The village locals must never have seen an American GI, as the old women and men pursed their lips and squinted at the three soldiers. At a pub, the men asked for a drink of whiskey and the barkeep, an elderly gent, cut them no slack whatsoever.

He said, "I don't have any whiskey. I have not seen

any in months. If I did have any, I wouldn't sell it to a bunch of *Damn Yanks*."

The men laughed and left the pub. Frank then stopped to buy some fish and chips, but thought the people were going to lynch him. They said he should eat his own food and leave theirs alone. Someone cursed and threw a handful of hot potatoes wrapped in newspaper at him. It was obvious the men were in the wrong place, so they quickly decided to leave the village.

The group split at the train station. Some went to London and Frank headed back to the base. At squadron HQ, he found a note awaiting him from Aunt Amy, who wanted him to come and visit her as soon as possible. The First Sergeant gave him another pass and Frank headed toward the mansion. He wondered why she wanted to see him—and why Ashly hadn't written the note. Had something happened to her? He rode his bike like the wind to get to the mansion as fast as he could.

Aunt Amy met Frank at the door, as if waiting for him, and from the look on her face, he confirmed that there was trouble.

"Where's Ashly? What's wrong? Let me see her," he demanded.

"Calm down, Frank, please."

"*Calm down*! Where is Ashly?"

"Come sit with me. Ashly's not here, Frank. We need to talk. Charles, bring us some hot tea, please."

Frank followed her into the parlor and Charles rushed in with the tea. This was the first time Frank had ever seen the butler in a hurry. As they sat, Aunt Amy began to sip her tea and Frank was sat there, *fit to be tied*, while waiting for her to continue her story. He didn't want any of the damned tea.

"There's no way to prepare you for what you are about to hear, Frank. Please try to stay calm and let me get my wits together. This is a long story and I don't know where to begin. You have proven to be such a fine young man. Listen to me carefully and please bear with me. There is so much that I cannot tell you, but I will say as much as I dare and you may discover more later. Someday I hope it will all make sense to you.

"Ashly has spent much time here with me. There was a good reason for you to meet her. She had to get away from the environment where she lived and her parents sent her here to stay with me. They knew she had to become a woman, which was something they could not handle. She learned well from me as I taught her about her body. I am sure you understand that part of what I am saying."

Amy sipped at her tea, and Frank fidgeted in his chair.

"Ashly needed to become a woman and you were selected for her. It was to be a casual affair, just once, but it did not turn out that way because she quickly grew to love you. She wanted you, but it would never have worked. Not only did Ashly love you, but I also saw something in you from my past. She told me that you know of the other painting—my one true love. Oh, how that hurts.

"Anyway, Ashly knew that if she was to have you it would have to be only by your portrait, so she painted you. She became miserable with the knowledge you would one day be gone from her life. She listened every morning when the American bombers went out and wondered if you were with them. She could hardly stand the thought that you might not return. She cried as she worked on your portrait and her tears are there, mixed with the paint. I heard you were able to see my Richard and wondered if he was trying to tell you something—something you will never know."

Amy paused, sipped more tea and stared at Frank.

"I didn't know she was so miserable," Frank said. "I thought there might be a way for us to be—well, closer. I was learning from her what love was all about. I've never been so close to anyone. I really don't know what to say or what to think. I guess maybe she thought the same thing would happen to me, as did with your Richard. Yes, I did think I saw Richard—several times, in fact."

"Let me continue. Ashly knew the romance was doomed from the start. Ashly is, of course, not her real name. It is a contraction of an old family name and she was told to use it in all meetings with you and others here about. Her family is of the elite here in Britain and it would be impossible for them to accept you because of their status. I wish it could be otherwise, but I have to agree, it's impossible. A plan was set before you two first met. Ashly, however, fell in love with you and grieved knowing what she had to do to you. She wanted to have you forever and the portrait will now be her only means to be with you. Come and see the painting she spoke to you about. I am proud of it and will never cover it again after this day. You will watch me reveal it and it will stay that way. You see, she taught me also."

Frank and Amy walked to the hall, where he knew there should have been a window. She reached for a cord and pulled the drape open. Instead of a window, there was a large painting, just as Ashly had described.

Amy switched on a portrait light and the painting came alive with color. There she was—Amy at the age of nineteen. She looked much like Ashly, even without her clothing, and the male figure *could have been Frank*!

The painting was showing age with hairline flaws. Amy and her Richard looked like Adam and Eve, painted in the most tasteful manner Frank had ever seen. It was rare art—museum quality. Tears came to Amy's eyes.

"If I had been as smart as Ashly, I would not have these tears," she said as she dabbed at her face. "I would have tried as she did."

"I don't understand."

"You will. Come with me."

Aunt Amy led Frank up the stairs to Ashly's room. She climbed the stairs slowly, causing Frank to think she was acting so much older than she had just days ago. He wondered if this situation was taking a toll on her. He knew that talking about her Richard had upset her.

At the top of the grand stairway, Amy leaned against the railing and gasped for breath. She looked at Frank and said, "Ashly will not be coming back, Frank. She vowed never to return to this house. She wants to remember you and everything that happened here. I am sure there will never be anyone else but you. She is so sorry for what she had to do."

He was not thinking clearly and did not know what to do or say. His Princess was gone, and he was devastated. What had happened to cause her to leave? Aunt Amy did not seem to be telling the whole story.

The door to Ashly's room was unlocked, so Aunt Amy pushed it open and stood back for him to enter. Then she followed him into the room. There in front of

Frank was the canvas-mounting frame with the portrait cut away. He walked to it and put his hand on the severed edge, moving it up and down. The portrait was gone, cut from the frame. Then he saw the painted canvas cut in strips and piled as if it were trash, and his heart fell in his chest at the sight. Amy let him stand there for a few silent moments before she spoke.

"Let me show you something before you think that she destroyed your portrait."

Amy moved the wooden frame to one side, away from the moleskin backdrop. She grasped the moleskin cloth, pulled it away and there before his eyes appeared another painting, one he had never seen before. This painting was larger than life, much larger than the one Frank had seen so often. He wondered why Ashly had worked so hard and the picture had never seemed finished.

This was the finished product!

Amy stepped back into the shadows as Frank looked in awe at the portrait before him. His touched it and knew the paint was long dry. He wondered when Ashly had finished this painting.

Standing before Frank was the most stunning painting he had ever seen. It was a portrait of him in the buff, standing over six feet in height in front of a dark background—probably the moleskin cloth. He could tell it had been painted at night, as the silver moonlight glistened over the wet body with shadows and flesh colors blending into the moonlighted beads of moisture. Part silver-white and part natural in color, it looked mystical. The silver light struck across the face, lighting it above all other, capturing his smile as if by camera. The hands, the toes, the entire anatomy were perfectly depicted, with the silver moonlight blending into his red hair. It was remarkable, a work worthy of a master. He was stunned and speechless as he looked in awe.

As far as Frank could tell, she was a master artist. He had never seen a painting where real flesh-tones and silver moonlight had been used. He stepped back and it was as if he were looking in a mirror. Yes, he had posed like that on a number of nights. The position of his arms and legs seemed the same as after she had corrected the spider-like painting he kidded her about. It was a remarkable painting—beautiful—even if it was of him, because the beauty of the artist shown through. As he looked closer, he noticed a silvery, moldy grape-colored spot on the left heel with blended colors of flesh tones. He would bear that bruise forever. She had captured his every feature, his humanity and his heart.

He turned and looked at the bed, which was made up as he had never before seen it, covered with a red and gold-fringed spread and royal blue shams. He turned back to the portrait, casting glances as he rotated so he would remember this room forever. The French doors that had stayed open were now closed and served as a reminder of so many pleasant evenings spent here with his Princess. Now Richard would again have this room to himself.

Dame Metcalf let Frank stand there and drink in Ashly's personification of the person she had known. She had poured her every artistic skill into the work before him. Was he already another ghost?

Frank turned and walked through the door with his chest heaving, unable to hide his emotions. Amy followed him, then turned to lock the door. Frank was ready to run from the mansion. His Princess was truly gone.

"Come, sit with me. There is more to tell," Aunt Amy said as they reached the bottom of the stairs. She led him into the parlor.

"Ashly could take it no longer. She knew her time here was up and she could never have you. If you were not killed, the Army would one day take you away from this land and she could not bear to see you part without her. She wanted you forever—you or a part of you. With the portrait, she will have you each day. She already made all the arrangements to have the portrait shipped to her place after you saw it. I will have that done this day. The men are standing by as we speak. Tonight it will be on its way."

Amy paused as if not wanting to go on with the talk.

"This painting will never be covered as was mine. It will be framed and mounted in a great hall, where dignitaries and heads of state will look upon your portrait. Still, none will know the true person in the painting. Only five people will ever know your identity."

"What are you saying? I seem to be missing something."

"Ashly is a very wealthy young woman. She owns several properties that put this place to shame. She is now a woman of her own. Yes, Frank, you will always be a part of her life, in more ways than you now know."

Frank looked at her, questioning what she meant by her statement of him being a part of Ashly's life. She was gone! He would never see her again, according to what Amy had just told him. Sure, the portrait might be with her, but not him. How could he be a part of her life?

"Frank, that portrait will hang with the great men in her family. Every family has secrets and her family is no different. This secret will be kept forever and the record will be that portrait of you. No record will be found elsewhere in all of time."

Frank understood hardly any of what Amy was saying.

"You looked odd when I said there would only be five people who knew the identity of the man in the picture. They are, of course, Ashly, you, Charles and me . . . and one other, who has not yet been named. I taught Ashly about her womanhood and she learned the lesson well. She knew what she was doing that first night when you came to her. It was all part of the plan. Yes, she knew exactly what to do that night when the two of you played in the garden, but she followed up just to be sure. You did not know?"

"Did not know . . . *what*?"

"That Ashly is *pregnant—with your child.* She conceived when you first took her womanhood. Had it not been so serious, I could have laughed aloud when Lieutenant Swartz told me you were sick every morning. You did not know because Ashly could not let you know and brushed aside your questions. You must remember this: never try to see this child—never. If you do, your life will be placed in danger. If you live, go back to America knowing that the child will receive the best of life. Maybe some day Ashly will disclose the story to the child. Of course, she will say you were killed in the war. None of this is your fault. She brought you to her at the proper time and you merely responded. So, be free of guilt. As with your ancestors, your descendants will live among the elite here in England. Be proud of yourself, young man. You have done more service than just for your country. You have brightened the life of many you will never know. Let this remain a mystery to ponder in your later years.

"Frank, you are welcome here at any time. Here is a key, a golden key, to Ashly's room. You and I are the only persons with such a key to that room. Once the room belonged to my Richard and me; now it belongs to Ashly and you. She said she will never return, but in my heart, I truly believe she will someday come here with her child to sit and remember you and this place. You, of course, may return only as does my Richard. Do you have any questions?"

Frank shook his head. He had hundreds of questions, but what could he ask? His head spun, yet not one question came forth. His heart was broken. He thought Ashly would be his lifetime lover. What had happened? A plan? What plan? He remembered they had investigated him before he met Ashly. Why? Were they not just two souls who had met and shared many pleasurable times of the heart—true companions? Now he knew he had no understanding of this thing called love. Ashly had shown him that love was not just sex. This hole in his chest—his baby? A part of him missing. Was this similar to the situation with the female marine? Why did Ashly run away? Who was this Princess?

Aunt Amy began speaking again. "Come, let us take you to base. I do not want you riding alone tonight."

Dame Metcalf had Charles stop some distance from the main gate. As Charles untied the bike from the boot, she said to Frank, "You are a good soldier, and a fine young man, Frank. Be kind to yourself."

Frank could only stand and stare at her as she said, "Goodbye, Frank."

All he could manage was "Goodbye."

Everyone was asleep when he returned to the hut, but Frank knew that sleep would be a long time coming for him this night. He went back outside and lay on the earthen mound of the bomb shelter. There was no moon, just the blackness of a world one step away from Hades as confusing thoughts crowded his mind. His life had been turned upside-down. Ashly, his Princess, had been taken—or had taken herself—from him.

Frank's mind pushed aside the cover from the top of the tomb where he buried his lost friends, and the painful memories of Lieutenant Butt and many others lost during these last few months seeped forth. The cool, hard earth of the air raid dugout beside the hut where he lay reminded him of the graves at Cambridge. He knew he had to put Ashly and his child in this tomb. He must be careful and not to slip or he might fall into the tomb with them. There would be no escape for him from that place. His body would be tied to a bed in a cell and force-fed while his mind mingled with the horrors of a never-ending nightmare.

"Go Ashly. Go! Join the other memories that I try to believe never happened. Just nightmares, all nightmares. I must try to learn more of this thing called love. Why doesn't someone help me? I need to understand. Goodbye Ashly. Goodbye, my love."

Carefully Frank lost hold on Ashly and her image and memory began to fade as he started replacing the heavy cover. They would all be gone. He would never remove the cover again. The pain—his very soul ached.

Dame Metcalf had known the danger of his flying, so why had she commented about his old age. He would probably be gone soon, the same as her Richard had left her. Maybe Richard was a harbinger of coming events for him, he considered.

There—the cover was in place. He thought to sit atop the cover, holding it shut. It was his private place and no one would ever find his tomb. He would treasure these people, their memories—always.

Frank lay on his back, trying with all his thoughts to set the memories in his mind so he could live with them. It was not an easy task. So many good times, the laughter, the fun, he was trying to make it hold. Only the best of times—remember them, for all else is gone. And yet? His baby? His Princess? Would they ever forget him?

He did not know when, but sleep finally came and he could not tell the difference between his thoughts and the dreams. He awoke sometime later and found that he had slept on the ground. He was cold and damp from the dew and needed coffee, hot coffee, and friendly company. Entering the hut, he found Alex in his bunk and shook him gently.

"Why are you getting me up so damn early? It's only five o'clock, and I got in late."

"Com'on, Buddy, let's get some coffee."

"Why so damned early?"

"I'll tell you after you're awake."

The September morning was cooler than usual. The water from the outside spigot was cold and snapped both wide-awake as they washed their faces. As they walked, Alex said, "Okay, Frank, what's up?"

"It's a long story. I need to tell you the whole thing. Think you're up to listening?"

"Damn right, shoot."

"Ashly's gone and I don't know what's happened."

"What? What're you saying? Ashly's gone? Is she . . . dead?"

"No, but she may as well be. Damn! I don't know where to start. I'm dead. No, that's not right—I'm just all screwed up."

"All right Frank, you've gotta start somewhere."

In the mess hall over two steaming cups of coffee, Frank began to tell the story about Ashly as best he could. Alex listened intensely and without interrupting.

"Man, that's some shit," he said when Frank finished. "I never heard anything like that. How do you feel about all that stuff? You tell me things Dame Metcalf said, but I don't see where they fit in with Ashly leaving the mansion."

"I slept on the shelter wall last night, Alex, if that lets you know. I had to think it out for myself. And you're right, there is a lot of that crap that don't make sense. I'm not being told the whole story."

CHAPTER 21

200th Mission Party

Alex and Frank stayed to themselves around the base that day, doing absolutely nothing. Alex would not leave Frank, even to go see Dana. He was a good listener and made Frank talk things out. He could see the pain his friend was suffering.

Then came news of a celebration on base. No gas, no bombs, no missions. It was time to celebrate the 200th Mission Party for the 385th Heavy Bomb Group. All four squadrons, 548th, 549th, 550th and 551st were put on military stand-down for three days. No missions—pray for good weather and have a good time.

The base commander, Colonel Van, called for his group to celebrate its 200th combat mission since arriving in England just over a year ago. The base was closed and spit-shinned for the affair. Wear your "Class-A" uniform, boys, they were told.

Two hangars were vacated, one for a beer party, the other for a stage show. One of the B-17s was parked near the entry to the flight line and made ready for visitors to enter and review. A complete English carnival was brought on base and set up near the hangars. There were motor-driven rides for the small children, and pony rides, and a Ferris wheel along with Fish and Chip vendors. An ice cream stand complete with American cones was raised along with penny gambling tables, weightguessers, clowns—the works were there for enjoyment. Just how the Colonel managed to arrange all this was a mystery, but if anyone could do it, he was the man.

Invitations were sent to the local people and to military Brass from both British and American forces. An Air Force general came on base to present medals, awards and commendations to the men of the 385th Bomb Group. An entire London burlesque show, The Windmill Theater with all stage props, would perform for the airmen after the public left the base.

The party started early in the day with British people being bussed to the base from surrounding villages. The children enjoyed the carnival's rides while the grown-ups helped drink the beer, eat fish and chips and inspect the B-17.

The officers and enlisted men were placed in revue formation as the General presented awards. It was questionable who enjoyed the open house party the most, the British or the men of the 385th.

The party was over for the public around 5:00 p.m. and the base was closed and secured. After supper the men of the 385th began to consume the balance of the beer and made ready to attend the stage show. The large hangar was filled to capacity when the burlesque show started. It was a remarkable show, with nothing left out from that performed in London. The several hundred men had a wild time as all the performers did their best to excite those attending. There was a law in England permitting men and women to perform nude on stage, as long as they did not move. With dim lighting, the people looked like statues.

The party was over around 10:00 p.m. and with all

the beer consumed a great time was had by all. Frank saw Dame Metcalf on the base but she was alone. He wondered why she was not with some of her card buddies but reasoned that may have been a bit much. Having heard she had someone check on him, he wondered if she might be working with the military on the spy thing.

The Dame had ignored Frank, but he saw her talking with several of the officers, apparently enjoying their company. The fact that she was able to get information on him was beginning to bother him—not that she had gotten the information, but why. Why did she have to know so much about him before arranging for him to meet Ashly?

Ashly was not as secure in Frank's mind as he had thought and her memory came forth when he saw some of the men on base with their English girlfriends. Ashly could be here also, he thought. There was something screwy about this whole situation. She could have his child, but not him. Why? Who was this Princess? Could Ashly have been the girl he had seen that first night in Scotland? She might have been, but if so, why had she chosen to follow him here to this base? Was the spy thing related? It just did not fit. There had to be some other reason for her to want him. He remembered her saying something about bloodlines. What had she meant?

"Get back in there," he thought as he pushed Ashly from his mind, unable to keep the cover on his mind tomb.

Alex and Frank drank some beer, but not much as it was flat English beer and they had to strain the hops out with their teeth as they drank it. But they had lots of fun. He kept remembering how well they got along. Again, he questioned love. Was it not just a perfect friendship with sex involved? He and Alex had the friendship, and he could get the other from female sources as needed. Ashly had failed to teach Frank enough about love, and his mind would not leave the subject alone. Was Alex's affair with Dana real love? Or were they just having the sex part of a relationship?

The airmen spent the day following the party draining the beer. More than 100 kegs had been consumed the day of the party and Aspirin became the big seller at the PX. On the day after the party, a loading list was posted for the next day's mission. Somehow, Frank's crew did not appear on the list—thank God.

The supply of bombs and fuel had been somewhat restored, but not all airplanes were yet ready to fly. The 385th had been requested to provide some airplanes to an adjacent group to make up a 35-plane formation.

The crew of the Horse was showing the strain of combat, with everyone on the crew changed drastically from when they had first arrived at the 385th. The pilot was keeping his distance from the other officers. The bombardier now spoke sharply to the enlisted men and was becoming a real pain. The co-pilot acted as if he had been force-fed crap for every meal and had a foul mouth. The replacement navigator never entered Frank's mind and was non-existent as far as he was concerned. He would never replace Lieutenant Butt.

Mark and Koop kept to themselves and stayed in their bunks most of the time. Don seemed all right; he wrote letters all the time and the officers were upset since they had to censor all letters. King was okay, but just not like his former self. And Alex? Well, there was nothing else in his world for him except Dana. Frank thought they were really in love, whatever love was.

It was not easy for Frank to find something on base to keep him going. Life had become miserable and he had to bury himself in his job. Only one thing pleased Frank. Some airmen that had been shot down over Germany and France were returning to England and these airmen were going from base to base giving lectures on how to survive and escape from the Germans. The Free French had an underground system right under the noses of the Germans. Airmen were sometimes captured and imprisoned as they landed after parachuting from bombers. Others managed to avoid capture and slip into the underground system.

The stories these men told could be helpful to men such as Frank in the event they were shot down. The airmen explained how to avoid capture by many dumb-sounding but workable ploys. The idea was to use one's brain and not be afraid to try anything. If an airman were captured out of uniform, the Germans would often shoot him as a spy. Some were shot although they were wearing their flight suits. Many airmen never lived to reach the ground because they either froze to death hanging high in the air or they died from lack of oxygen because of the same reason. The men were taught to drop until they saw the ground moving before opening their parachute, which would place them at about 2-3,000 feet above ground; lower if possible, to avoid being seen.

Once on the ground and if not injured, an airman might have a chance to avoid capture. Many German citizens, however, would shoot an American on sight. The idea was to avoid being seen for as long as possible in the event the underground people were in the area. Some Germans and most French people would help a downed airman even if it put their lives on the line.

Many airmen were hidden in peoples' homes, which risked the lives of all. The French became skeptical of airmen as the Germans started using their people as undercover agents to trap the French with a habit of aiding downed fliers, and many French people were caught and killed.

A program was set up on base to help airmen in the event they were shot down. Passport photographs were taken. The men were required to let their hair grow for several weeks and clean faces were not allowed for the photo. A white shirt, necktie and old suit coat were provided with side and front shots made for a photo, which was carried with the airmen on every mission. In case they escaped capture, the photos would be turned over to the underground to make a German ID card.

The men were provided with a new pair of low-quarter shoes just like the ones manufactured in Germany. These shoes were worn on base to scuff off the newness and the airmen carried them, along with their passport photos, tied to their parachute so they went along with the men when they bailed out of their falling bombers.

Then there were the lessons in speaking the German language. Each man was taught to say and understand certain spoken German phrases such as: "I want a bowl of cabbage, I don't know, Sorry, Thank you and others such as *Gott im Himmel, Gott dammt, Ver dammt, or Ver wunschen.*

Every man had to recite these German phrases, and it brought a big laugh when Frank with his quiet southern drawl spoke in German. No way would he get away with trying to sound like a German. It was a lost cause for him to try and overcome his southern heritage. He was told just to act dumb and this brought more belly laughs from all the airmen. Being laughed at was not so bad. At least he knew where he stood if he survived after jumping from a bomber and had to mix with the Germans. In fact, he sort of enjoyed giving the men something to laugh about.

CHAPTER 22

The Final Days

The long break from combat was finally over, as the crew of the Horse found their names on the loading list for another mission. It had been seventeen days since the crew had last flown a mission, which was time enough for them to realize how lucky they had been and how they hated to start the missions all over again. Everyone had encountered many chances to receive their ticket to hell. Lieutenant Butt and many others had cashed in their chits. Frank realized how great the odds were of his not finishing the 35 assigned combat missions. The trips to the Cambridge cemetery had been on hold but that would likely change this day.

As the crew prepared for the mission, Frank expected to see Ashly everywhere he looked. "God, what am I doing standing here by this airplane? There are so many other places I'd rather be," he thought.

Just then, he heard Alex let out a string of curse words. He looked up and saw Alex holding his hand out the waist window with blood dripping from a finger. Before he could move, blood dripped on Frank's flight-suit collar.

"What the hell happened?" he asked Alex.

"I mashed my *Gott* damn finger slamming the cover on this *Gott* damned machine gun."

Frank met Alex as he jumped from the waist door. "Here, let me wrap this handkerchief around it."

"You didn't blow your nose on it, did you?"

"No, it's clean! Stand still."

"Don't get nasty with me. It's my damn finger and it hurts."

"I said stand still, fool. You're getting blood on me. Hold this tight while I get a bandage."

"You'd better hurry or I'll bleed to death."

Frank went to the emergency bag, found a bandage and wrapped it around Alex's mashed finger. It was not cut all that badly; it had just bled a lot. The bandage and some pressure quickly stopped the bleeding.

"You're some kind of a doctor. Messy as all hell."

"I'm the best you've got so shut your mouth. Want me to sew it up for you?"

"Hell no!" Alex said and they both laughed.

"It'll get well before you get married."

"Shut your mouth! Next week if all goes as planned."

No more was said as the crew finished preparing for the mission. Alex and Frank walked away from the Horse and lit up cigarettes. King and Koop joined them and all were quiet.

The summer sun was reaching the fall solstice and left the sky dark as the Horse struggled with the bomb load of six 1000-pound bombs. It was all she wanted this day. The Horse never complained except for her creaks and groans as the cold wind found a way through the aging metal. Frank sat back and let the airplane talk to him. He had learned to tell her state by the feel of minor vibrations as the engines synchronized. The constant drone played a melody when all was right. He knew every vibration was telling him the condition of the airplane.

There was a familiar odor in the airplane with which he had learned to live. He knew it all too well. The odor was a mixture of many things, although his nose could separate each: gas, burnt gunpowder, hydraulic fluid, gun oil, hot insulation on wiring, a musty odor from mould spores hiding in unseen places, urine from when a relief tube overflowed, the cutting, acrid scent of blood, sweat, the putrid aroma of where someone had up-chucked, the flight suit odor, cigarette smoke, and many others. Each odor elicited a memory, each memory a story in itself.

The Horse climbed higher in her domain of the dark morning sky as Frank jotted in his notes: Tuesday, September 19, D-Day +105. He was snug in his ball turret as the electrically heated flight-suit gave much comfort over the older fur-lined one—unless a short occurred. He remembered almost freezing to death wearing one of these just after they were issued.

The formation was gathering into a full wing of 105 B-17 heavy bombers, heading toward the same target. Once there they would split into three groups and hit separate targets. The formation was going to Koblenze, Germany, where the 385th was to take out a major bridge over the Rhine River. The other two groups were to bomb the city and a steel manufacturing plant.

As usual, heavy anti-aircraft batteries fired at them along the route to the target, and near the city, a German fighter squadron came into view. Fortunately, the P-51 fighter escort cut them off before they reached the formation of bombers. Frank watched the dogfight until his group reached the IP and started the bomb run. A huge black cloud formed in front of the bombers as guns opened fire on them.

Through the smoke, Frank spotted the bridge—a huge structure with towers at both ends. Flak pounded close to the Horse but the aircraft received only slight damage as the bomb bay doors opened. The airplane was bouncing from the concussion of the bursting shells, making it difficult for the pilots to hold formation.

Frank watched as the 1000-pounders fell on the bridge and started exploding. The smoke and debris from multiple explosions all but hid the target as it and the surrounding areas were pulverized. He turned the turret and watched the bombs from the other two groups hitting the city and plant, sending great plumes of smoke drifting skyward from the burning buildings. The bridge and surrounding areas had been destroyed by the onslaught of bombs dropped from the B-17s and fires raged in the bombed buildings. As the formation reached the Rally Point, Frank looked back and saw that the towers at each end of the bridge were still standing—but the bridge itself was no more. The city was ablaze with raging fires everywhere that he could see.

Frank switched his intercom over to the command radio and listened for a few seconds. It seemed the formation commander was getting his ass chewed out by some general back in England. The gist of what Frank heard was that a troop general had not wanted that bridge bombed and had tried to stop the formation commander from dropping the bombs. The general had not used the correct code words for his transmission and the commander did not obey the order not to drop.

Frank thought, "Sorry sir, that bridge ain't no more, and the city ain't in much better shape."

The men would learn later that the troop general

wanted to save the bridge so that when American troops advanced in that area later, they could use it to cross the river.

The Cambridge cemetery would be busy this weekend as there were many dead and wounded men returning to base from this mission. Frank had no idea how many B-17s had been lost over the targets. The Horse had lost an engine but received no other major damage and no one was injured. Frank again thanked his Guardian Angel.

The formation picked up a fighter escort on the way back to base and Frank did not see any German fighters on the way home. He stayed in the ball turret until the formation was over the English coast where the pilot came over the intercom and said the men could remove their oxygen masks.

The 1-1/2 ounces of Scotch whiskey was welcomed at the mess hall. Frank noticed he was not the only one picking over the food. The 17-day layoff without flying had taken some of the pressure off the men but it was now back in full force—and they had four more missions to go.

The crew of the Horse had three days rest to think about their last four missions, and tension ran high while they waited. No one wanted to talk about these final missions. Men were dying around them every day, and the hut had lost two more crews so everybody was tense and stayed to themselves. The strain was showing as small fights broke out among airmen in Frank's and other huts.

Then came another loading list.

Friday, September 22, 1944, Mission number 32, D-Day +108.

The target was a Tiger tank factory located at Kassel, Germany. The flight would be at 26,000 feet, 6-1/2 hours with 5-1/2 hours on oxygen. The outside air temperature would be around 55 degrees below zero. They would carry a mixed bomb load of five 500-pound general demolition and five 500-pound incendiaries.

The briefing officer said this factory was turning out tanks that were taking a deadly toll on our troops, and it must be destroyed. The group was not to worry too much about hitting the plant; a miss would be all right, as the plant workers lived adjacent to the factory. It was a difficult situation for the Germans, although they would have a chance to destroy many American bombers. It was estimated there were ninety anti-aircraft guns defending the area and it would be a long bomb run.

Frank made a quick calculation in his head: 90 guns at 3 shells per minute times 10 minutes on the bomb run would equal 2700 rounds of anti-aircraft shells. Now that was a lot of flak—not as bad as some targets, but enough if the gunners were on the ball.

As the Horse approached the target, Frank realized that all ninety guns were in operation. Soon the sky turned black from bursting shells and the Horse was jarred time after time when concussions wracked the airplane and shrapnel cut through the aluminum body. Whether by mistake or planned, the bombs strung across the factory and hit in the housing area of the workers, causing a real firestorm from the many incendiary bombs.

Several of the 385th airplanes would not fly for a few days, as there had been lots of damage on the Kassel mission. It was a scramble by maintenance to secure spare parts for repairs. *Buy, beg, borrow or steal*, was the old adage Frank heard when he was younger, and this seemed to be the norm for the ground crews. Losses of men and spare parts were greater than the supply these days. Several airplanes from the 385th flew with another group for a "make-up" formation, since all the bases were having a similar problem getting parts.

The group of airplanes ran into disaster as the formation encountered stiff head winds on the return from the target and ran short of gas. As luck would have it, the ground troops had taken a field in Belgium the day before and the bombers were able to land on that airfield. The Air Ferry Command brought the men from the 385th back to a base in southern England where they could be returned to their own base. The bombers were returned a few days later. No one could explain the reason for not knowing about the strong winds.

The new replacement crews coming to the base seemed to be getting younger. Some of the gunners had been in the Army only six months and they thought they were real warriors. They did not know *doodly-squat* about what they were getting into. Frank hated to see them get shot down so quickly, as most of the newer crews made less than five missions before being lost over Germany. The German anti-aircraft gunners seemed to be more accurate even than just a month ago.

The veteran fliers' refusal to talk to the youngsters did not help. One young airman spouted off to Frank and he would have liked to smack the boy, who was a real smart-ass. That man and his crew went down on their first mission and it really got to Frank, since they bunked in the same hut. The young smart-ass was nicknamed Red.

The group had a few days down-time and passes were allowed, so Alex and Frank took off for London. Frank knew that Alex was worried about Dana's health and he talked nonstop about her during the train ride. He had not heard from her in several days but reasoned that could be because of the slow British mail system.

When the train stopped at Paddington Station, Alex took off in a dead run to see Dana, leaving Frank far behind. He was in a taxi before Frank even reached the station door. They had made plans to meet there tomorrow for the afternoon train back to base. Alex wanted time alone with Dana and Frank hoped Nichole would help him forget about Ashly.

Going to see Nichole was interrupted at the station door as Frank saw a marine captain walking toward him, carrying her bags. Could it be her? As she drew near, he confirmed that this was indeed Captain Ann Hudson. She dropped her bags and ignoring military protocol, she and Frank embraced and kissed right there before God and everybody. Although it had been almost a year since that night they met on the troop train in Abilene, neither of them had forgotten. Damn, this had to be the surprise meeting of the war. He held her back and each looked the other over from head to toe.

"You sure don't look like that young corporal I remember from a year ago," she said. "The rank, the ribbons, the wings—you've been busy I see. You look great in that tailored uniform instead of the other sackcloth outfit."

"Yeah, and it seems you've had a change of mind, *Captain*. You look great and those double bars don't hurt a bit."

Then they both started talking at the same time.

"We can't stand here and discuss our private lives. Let's go to my hotel where we can talk. Do you have time?"

"Bet your ass I—excuse me, ma'am ... you bet I do—yes ma'am, sir."

Throughout the taxi ride and check-in, Frank carried her bags as if he were her aide. No questions were asked at the desk. He felt he could carry her and her bags. Once in the room the questions flowed.

"What happened? You seemed set on getting pregnant, a medical discharge, and now I see you're a captain."

"Long story, soldier. The plan was working, but three months after we parted I was getting off a train and took a bad fall. Wound up in a hospital with a miscarriage. I almost died. The doctor helped me when I was released from the hospital. He knew some Brass and they pulled a few strings so I was given a job in Washington. Met some Brass there and my career took off—and *NO*, I did not sleep my way up. The people I met were very nice and I began to enjoy Army life. I spent several months in DC learning my new assignment. I've found a new role in life that I'm pleased with. It's very interesting work. I'm here on business, but I can't discuss it."

"Damn, from shuttling recruits to secret service. That's really great. I remember you scared the crap out of me back there in Texas, but it was worth it. I'll never forget any part of that night. You being an officer scared the hell outta me."

"You seem a little more sure of yourself now. I like it. I guess you've spread your wings, so to speak."

Frank told her of his life after Texas, the training and his combat missions. He added a little about some of the girls he'd met but did not mention the nude acts before Ashly and Nichole. That might come later if the situation called for such talk. A person would have thought they were family catching up on news after a long separation. The conversation went on for over an hour before he asked if she would like to go to dinner. He had learned that lesson well!

After dinner, she had a glass of wine but he abstained—a part of the same lesson. He was looking for an opening to settle the room thing when she asked, "You will stay here with me tonight, won't you?"

Jackpot!

She had a second glass of wine and soon the combination of the wine, the good food, and Frank's southern drawl had in effect removed the Captain bars and Sergeant stripes, leaving only two lonely people far from home. She was aware of the sweat and he remembered the odor of "Military Brass." That same odor. Maybe Nichole did know what she was talking about. He still used the Lifebuoy soap and it mixed well with her scent. They were both slim and trim from the military rat race, and they were ready for action. It became obvious that Ann had not slept with a man in a long time, maybe not since Texas, and was trying to make up for lost pleasures. A dim lamp lighted their bodies, casting large shadows on the wall, animated and vocalized by her pleasant uttering. It was a long and enjoyable night.

The next day after lunch, Ann told Frank, "I have to meet some people before dinner. I wish it could be otherwise but business must come first. There is a lot I would like to tell you but I can't. I can only say this: we're looking for a leak of information to the Germans at an airbase, but I must stop there. Be careful, you are a fine soldier."

Their parting was bittersweet. Both were glad their paths had crossed again, and neither had any hang-ups about military rules. Fate had dealt them a winning hand. Captain Hudson left for the embassy in a taxi and Sergeant Mays waved goodbye.

It was only an hour before the train was scheduled to leave for Stowmarket as Frank walked toward the station. He had no time for Nichole on this trip. He disliked not seeing her but it just was not in the cards. The meeting with Ann lay well between his ears. He thought it had helped keep the cover on the tomb in his mind. The memories of his earlier year were much easier to deal with than these last five months. Damn, why did that have into pop into his head? No, the tomb cover was not all that well in place as it moved and thoughts of Ashly and all the others came rushing back to the forefront. He managed to put them aside as he smiled to himself at the memory of meeting Ann and her being so glad to see him again. Just maybe he could get on with his life after Ashly.

At the station, Alex slapped him on the back and said, "Shit man, you look like you just lost your best friend. Did something go wrong between you and Nichole?"

Frank laid the story of Captain Ann on him in full detail—the whole nine yards, all the way back to Texas.

"Good Lord, man! Don't you know they could hang you for screwing around with an officer? I'd better be careful or the Brass will have my ass, thinking I'm the same as you."

Alex laughed and that made it all right. There were no better two friends anywhere in the world. They could do no wrong to each other. Their paths had come together in Dyersburg almost a year ago and it had been a solid friendship ever since. They looked out for each other more than Frank and his brother ever had.

Once more, Alex was filled with news about Dana. The paperwork was completed for their wedding on his next trip to London. They were so happy because of the expected child. She would have to see a doctor as soon as she started showing.

The train ride to Stowmarket didn't seem so long as Alex talked about Dana and his future planes during the entire trip.

CHAPTER 23

Missions Number 33 and 34

Alex did not tell anyone else on the crew about his wedding plans, and Frank would have died before he betrayed his friend's trust by telling anyone. It was Alex's business and it would stay that way as far as Frank was concerned.

Several days passed and all Alex talked about was Dana, except when he kidded Frank about shacking-up with an officer. It seemed to give Alex great pleasure to see that Frank was getting over Ashly and the child, though.

As the Horse left the runway, Frank got busy scribbling notes of the day's mission. All the gunners stayed hunkered down close to each other, sharing body heat. The others had gotten used to seeing him writing his notes and they said nothing about it.

Tuesday, October 3, 1944, Mission number 33, D-Day + 119. This mission was to bomb an airfield at Gelbelstadt, Germany with twelve 500-pound bombs at 25,000 feet. S-2 Intelligence had information that Germany had a jet airplane—an airplane without propellers. What in hell kind of airplane could fly without propellers? Frank thought this must be something like the *Buzz Bombs* he had experienced in London. How little he knew.

The jet was not yet ready for combat but was in flying

condition. It seemed the fuel consumption had not been worked out for the craft to remain airborne for any great length of time. Today's target was the sole airfield for these new type airplanes.

The Horse was airborne before daylight. Why so damned early, Frank wondered? The Army was as bad as hospitals, with every day having to start early. When Frank had been hospitalized in Dyersburg with the flu, some bastard was waking him early every morning, as if he had somewhere to go and was already late.

There had been light flak along the way to the target, but with little damage. As the bomb bay doors opened, heavy flak hit the formation and then stopped, having lasted less than a minute, which was odd. Below and ahead Frank could see the target area and airplanes were taking off from the grassy runways. These were short stubby-looking airplanes such as he had never seen before. They had a streak of fire and smoke coming from their tails.

In less than two minutes, the airplanes were at formation level, but out of gun range. He could not believe the planes had climbed to the elevation of over 20,000 feet in such a short time. It had required less than three minutes for the German airplanes to reach their altitude. They circled the formation of bombers once and then flew away, with neither the German planes nor the bombers firing a single shot.

When the bombs hit the target, there were many secondary explosions. Some bombs exploded in the nearby river, but the ground target was destroyed. As the formation of bombers crossed the river and flew over a small town, the flak started again. When the bombs were dropped, the flak had been way off to one side with none near the Horse and Frank wondered why there had not been defense guns at the airport proper.

The group did not have fighter escort on this mission, which was just as well, as the German fighters flew away at a speed greater than any airplane Frank had ever seen.

On their return to base, Frank came close to getting busted in rank. The bombardier decided to relieve himself and did not tell Frank to turn his turret to the rear, which he should have done. The stream of urine came back on the turret sight glass and froze instantly, resulting in an argument between Frank and the bombardier that the pilot had to stop. Frank sat in the radio room after telling the bombardier to come back and fly the *gott* damn ball turret. He was ready to whip the bombardier's ass.

Six days passed and no one was allowed to leave the base. Everyone questioned why there were no passes and Alex, who was outraged, went to squadron HQ frequently. The wedding was being postponed for some unknown reason. The mail between Great Ashfield and London was slow and letters from Dana were a week getting to Alex.

A list was finally posted for mission number 34. This and one more—only two more chances to be killed. For some reason, Frank felt this might be the one, and he was really down as he recorded the mission statistics: October 9, 1944, Mission number 34, D-Day + 124. The target was a buzz bomb factory at Gustausburg, Germany, to be bombed from an altitude of 24,000 feet with five 1000-pound bombs.

The summer sun had lost its warmth and it was chilly in the morning darkness. At 5:00 a.m., the crew was loading guns on the Horse. All were quiet as they went about their chores of getting ready. Frank finished, walked away from the airplane and smoked several cigarettes. He felt so alone and continued to look for Ashly every place he went, even on the flight line.

A *Buzz Bomb* factory! The cover over the tomb in Frank's mind slid open a crack. That other buzz bomb raid and Lieutenant Butt popped into the front of his mind. He thought of his Guardian Angel and wondered if this would be the mission in which his luck would run out. Or would his Angel take over and again save the day?

The briefing officer said the thick cloud cover would require use of the new IFR bombsight today, which could see through the clouds and find the target. Great Ashfield was completely covered by clouds and Frank never saw the ground after takeoff. All other bombers were required to drop their bombs following the lead of the airplane with the IFR bombsight. This meant the bombardiers would not use their bombsights, which would render them useless, unless they had to fire their machine guns.

As the bomber formation climbed through the cloud cover, the sky became lighted by the morning sunlight. The tops of the clouds were as smooth as if spread with a spatula, and extended to the horizon in every direction. Above the clouds, the sky was bright blue, as if just washed.

Frank always kept his turret moving as he watched the skies for any object on the move. On this mission, he was to see a sight that few people are privileged to observe. From the direction of the flight, the sun was at 4 o'clock high. At 10 o'clock low were the shadows of all the airplanes in the formation as they moved across the cloud tops. He could pick out the shadow of each bomber and knew its position in the formation. The shadow of the Horse appeared at the center of a full circular rainbow and he stared at this sight that he would never forget. The cloud tops looked like fiery opal and the rainbow colors were extremely bright and vivid, almost fluorescent. The rainbow contained all the colors of the spectrum with reds to the outside and blue in the center around the shadow of Frank's airplane. It was awesome and Frank could think only about what he had seen. He had made comments about his Guardian Angel but now he questioned whether this was something into which he should put more thought. He pondered the question; did his Guardian Angel have a hand in this sighting? The ghosts in Frank's memory seemed to say there was some connection. Perhaps this sight was for him to understand that each man's life is different, in that each has a unique mission while alive here on earth.

CHAPTER 24

Disaster Strikes

The first pilot had flown his 35 missions and was now grounded. Before being allowed to take his normal crew into combat, he had flown his first mission as co-pilot with another crew to gain experience. That training mission had put him one ahead of all other men on the crew and the others still had one more combat mission to fly. The pilot was sent from the base to a center somewhere in England.

The remaining eight men were now known as *spares*, each man having one more mission to complete their tour of duty. Their last mission would be flown with a crew of strangers, as they would replace any man on another crew who could not fly his mission. This type of life was a living hell for the men of Frank's crew, with no more buddies on a mission. A crewman's name would be placed on a list to replace a man, and at the last minute, the other man might show up. It was nerve wrenching at best and the men lost sleep and were nervous. Alex could not get away to wed Dana so he wrote her a letter and Frank went with him to have it censored and mailed.

This life started on October 10 and lasted for several days before two of the men actually went on a mission: Lieutenant Slater and Alex. Frank awakened the morning Alex was leaving the hut and as Alex started out the door, he turned and gave Frank the sergeant's left-handed salute. Of course, there was no more sleep for Frank this morning. He wished he could be going with his buddy because it was not right for Alex to be out there all alone.

Frank had only said, "See ya," as Alex left the hut.

After lunch, Frank went to the flight line and discovered that the mission Alex and Slater had gone on was to Berlin. He thought, "My God, of all the places to go, why Berlin?" He thought of his Guardian Angel and asked that Alex be watched over. As Frank sat there sweating the group back to base, he had too much time to think, and while waiting, he thought of all the good times he and Alex had shared.

A crowd began to gather as time came for the bombers to be back at base. At around 2:00 p.m., the flight line started to liven, but Frank had already been there an hour waiting for his friend to return. First came the roar of engines and then there they were, B-17s circling the base, allowing the planes with dead and wounded to land first. Fire trucks were putting out fires on some bombers while ambulances picked up men from others. Thirty-five airplanes had gone out, and only thirty-two were counted back in.

Three missing! Where was Alex's plane? Frank could not locate it and panic set in as he ran around looking for his friend's plane. Perhaps there had been some mistake and Alex had flown in a different plane. Frank finally went to the ground command officer and asked.

"Sergeant Mays, I'm afraid that airplane is among the missing. Let's go over to debriefing and find out what we can."

A pilot reported seeing the bomber shot down and said he did not see any parachutes coming from the airplane as it fell over Berlin. Other men reported similar sightings. So it was official; the airplane was missing in action. Without a word, Frank turned and walked out of the briefing. He leaned his forehead against the building wall, hardly able to breathe.

"No! No! No! It can't be! Not Alex . . . nooooo," he yelled when he finally drew a breath.

Frank ran from the flight line to the hut, a distance of almost a half-mile. He fell on his bunk and cried his heart out. The other men on the crew came in and tried to calm him, but he had to get it out. As he cried, all the memories ran before his mind and then came the image of Dana. Dana! That thought stopped his tears. Dana! My God! Dana and the baby! What will happen when she finds out about Alex? There was no way for her to know unless he went to London and told her. Since the Army could not contact her, a trip was necessary, and Frank knew he must go now. He would have to get a pass from the squadron commander, which would take him off the flight list. Every man was needed, so he decided to approach the First Sergeant and have him plead his case with the commander.

Frank stopped at the basin and washed his face, then went to the First Sergeant, who listened patiently to Frank's story. When Frank finished, the sergeant went to the CO and secured a pass for Frank to go to London. He alone would be allowed to leave the base. Could he make it alone? Yes, he would make it if he had to crawl.

Lieutenant Slater had been lost on the same mission and on the same airplane, but this had not yet registered on Frank's mind. Alex was the one who was his best friend and he was going to have to deliver this awful news to Dana. Nothing else in the world mattered now.

Frank did not remember Dana's address and would have to ask Nichole to go with him. Anyway, Dana would need her help when Frank told her the news.

Frank changed clothes and picked up his pass. The others wished him good luck on his trip.

It seemed the train would never get to London. It was late and Nichole would probably be at her flat. Everything had slowed and the whole world had gone wrong. Gone to hell! There were no tears when Frank reached Nichole's flat. When she opened the door, she saw Frank looking at her as if she were not even there. He was seeing something beyond, on which only his eyes could focus.

In his quiet southern drawl he spoke, "Hello, Nichole . . . I need to talk with you."

Tears crept down her cheeks. She had never before seen Frank this way: no hug, no kiss, nothing. He seemed to be functioning on instinct as he, in a soft unnatural voice, told Nichole about Alex and that he had to see Dana and let her know. He did not know how to say the words to Dana and wanted Nichole to go with him, thinking that Dana would need her. Yes, he was all right, he told her, just awfully tired.

Nichole let him sit for a minute and rest. He would need to listen to her carefully and she did not think he was listening to anything but what was in his head as he stood to go.

"Frank, there's something you don't know. Now sit back down. Sit down, Frank, and listen to me!"

Nichole knew he was not hearing her words so she quickly kissed him and that made him pay attention at her. Now that she had his attention, she spoke quickly.

"Frank, Dana's in the hospital. She's very ill. Frank, look at me! I have listened to your story, now you listen to me. Frank, Dana is near death."

His jaw dropped. He stiffened. She had his full attention now.

"What—what did you just say?"

"Dana is near death. Her family is with her now. She will not be able to hear what you have to say about Alex. When I last saw her about an hour ago, she was still in a coma. There was no way to contact Alex this morning when she went to hospital. I was supposed to meet her this morning at her place. We were to do an early shift at the club. I almost knocked down her door thinking she was asleep. I finally located her hidden key and let myself in. She was lying unconscious in the bathroom and blood was everywhere.

"Dana had a tubal pregnancy and she hemorrhaged. I tried to find help and finally had a neighbor call an ambulance. She had lost so much blood by then that she was near death. They rushed her to hospital and then contacted her family through the Bobbies. I had just arrived here when you came. I left the hospital after her family arrived and they promised to let me know if there was a change in her condition."

Nichole had just finished saying these words when there came a loud knock on her door. She opened the door and a man handed her a note. When she read it, she burst into tears. Frank guessed what the note had read and picked it up to confirm his assumption. Dana had died just after Nichole left.

The two stood there holding each other. What could

he say? What was he to think? Maybe Alex and Dana were now together. That was what Alex had wanted most in this world, for him and Dana to be together, and now they were—forever.

Nichole jumped when Frank loudly said, "YES!" An image had passed before his mind and he thought he saw Alex smile at him. "Yes!" he repeated.

It was all right now. He knew that his best friend was with his Dana, walking hand-in-hand, looking back over his shoulder and smiling at Frank. Everything was all right. Alex and Dana were together.

He told Nichole what had passed before his mind's eye and she agreed it must be true. Frank questioned whether this was more of his Guardian Angel's doings. "How God works his miracles," he thought.

The note stated that the family was arranging to take Dana home to the country for burial and they wanted to leave London as soon as possible. They would understand that Nichole could not make the funeral.

Nichole and Frank lay on the bed and went over the events that caused them to lose their friends. Apollo would remain absent this night as he mourned his lost friends.

Frank, of course, could not sleep. He could not stop thinking of how he and Alex had confided in each other, each always telling the other the most intimate details of their life, for no other reason than they trusted each other with their very lives. There would be no more smiles, no more laughter, no more poking fun at each other, no more bragging of female conquests, no more borrowing of toothpaste, no more listening to the other's problems, no more numbers on a white marker to kneel at, and no more talk of plans for Dana and him. No more Alex. No godfather. No nothing.

For the first time in a while, the sun was up before Frank. He had finally let sleep come to him and it brought troubled dreams. The weight of the world was upon his shoulders as in the cool October sun, Nichole and Frank walked the old ways where Alex had been with Frank. The streets of London were no longer the same. Piccadilly Circus was quiet. The orators in Hyde Park were silent. People went about their business as usual in a city that was bombed nightly. There were so few people on the streets now.

They had a lunch of tea and sweet rolls at the Red Cross Club. Frank's pants were getting loose in the waist as he continued to lose weight ounce-by-ounce. At the American Bar, Frank purchased a bottle of whiskey and a bottle of white wine. He said something nonsensical about them representing Alex and Dana. He would have to get drunk. Dead drunk. He had to stop this grinding in his mind. Maybe he would get some sleep in a drunken stupor. Maybe then the nightmares would go away. The cover of the tomb in his mind was ajar and ghostly images clouded his senses. There had been no screams from Alex. Just silence. Just that last smile.

The sun had set when Frank thought about Nichole not having eaten. He took her to the restaurant with the roving band, which again played Grecian music for Nichole and he saw the hurt in her eyes. She was losing her friends the same as he was his, and he knew she was remembering her Alfred.

Frank ordered something from the menu with the name of "Victory Steak," which turned out to be a slice of Spam wrapped in bacon and fried. He laughed for the first time as he thought of what Alex might have said about his choice of food. Nichole drank down her glass of wine. She knew that Frank's laugh announced that he was back with her. Apollo just might show up this night. Her Zeus would be pleased with them.

When they returned to her flat, Frank set the whiskey aside as there was no need for it. He was beginning to feel better as the deaths now hid somewhere deep in his mind. Besides, drink might get in the way of having a good time. He would celebrate just as Alex would want him to do. There had been enough hurt in their lives.

Frank had another hot tub bath and felt freshly clean both inside and out. No booze was needed. He was himself again. This was the way Alex would have wanted him to act. The cool night air drifted through the window cooling the sweat as it seeped from his skin. His emotions had made room for an amorous exculpation.

They awoke with a start. The blackout drape had fallen from the window and the panes were shaking as if they would shatter. Loud noises and flashes of light strobbed the room as Frank realized they were in the midst of an air raid, and must be near ground zero! Nichole screamed and he held her close, as it was too late now to run for cover. He questioned what he could do to calm her and kissed her repeatedly, causing him to become aroused. Her tears went away as Apollo amorously quieted her fears.

The noise of the bursting bombs finally moved farther away, then the sounds of the all-clear wailed, and they rested. They spent the rest of the day in and around

Nichole's flat until time for Frank to leave and return to base

The train ride back to Stowmarket was a trip Frank should not have made alone, as his ghosts were not as well contained as he had thought. He wept, the tears now coming freely. The conductor asked if he was all right and he managed to nod his head. There were empty seats in the car but an elderly British woman came to sit beside him and put her hand on his shoulder. It was comforting and neither said a word. He did not have to tell her why he cried; somehow, she understood.

At the base, he told the crewmen about Dana, and for the first time, they knew part of the story and understood why Alex always took off for London. He told only portions of the story, though, as he felt it was not their business. Alex would have wanted it that way. They would not have truly understood and these were now Frank's treasured memories.

The days passed slowly as Frank coped with the situation of flying his last mission. The other men in his crew seemed as anxious as he was about their last mission. Frank's name had appeared on three loading lists but all three times the missing airman had showed up at the last minute. And all three times, the airplane Frank was scheduled to fly in was shot down over Germany and all crewmen onboard the airplanes were lost. All three times, Frank was also listed as "missing-in-action" as his name was still on the flight manifest. This required much effort to have his name cleared and one time the quartermaster even came to pick up his clothing, as Frank sat on his bunk. Twice he had to stop them from sending the dreaded telegram to his mother.

Satan was about to get another shot at him. On the night of October 16, his name appeared on another list, and this time he would fly his final mission—number 35.

CHAPTER 25

The Final Mission

Tuesday, October 17, 1944, Mission number 35, D-Day + 133.

It was a morning like so many others, yet this would be a day Frank would never forget. It would be his final combat mission, and he felt so alone. The air was crisp as he walked to the airplane. He lit a cigarette and looked around while waiting for the gun carrier to bring the machine guns.

In briefing, Frank had met the crew he was to fly with, and he did not like what he saw and heard. This was a totally green crew, having arrived at Great Ashfield just three days ago. The pilot had not even flown as co-pilot on a single mission. They were nine excited, *green-ass* flyboys.

This crew had not received all the training, as Frank had before being sent overseas, and he questioned why HQ was sending him on his last mission with a green crew. It was a real kick in the ass to think they cared so little about him. This was not standard procedure—his last mission and their first. It had never been this way with others flying their final mission. Alex and Slater had been placed on a seasoned crew. Was someone hoping he would get shot down? He felt like this might be *get-even* day—a real screw-Frank day!

The gunners were having problems putting their guns

in place and Frank went over to help them. Not a single man could get his guns installed correctly and he had to help them all with such a simple task. Frank began to sweat as he realized what a mess he was getting into, and he was glad there were not so many German fighters as there had been just weeks ago.

This B-17 was a new airplane, a "G" model, with bright shiny aluminum everywhere—not at all like the old War Horse. Why did he have to remember that just now? He missed his crew and their airplane, the War Horse, which had been turned over to another crew and was now taking care of her new men.

Memories of the crew and their first mission came to his mind. They had been so young and happy back then, with not an inkling of what lay ahead—perhaps just like this crew. He remembered the piece of flak in his boot and the bruise that showed up in the painting. Well, it had not all been bad. There had been his Princess, Ashly, and of course, Dame Metcalf and Swartz. And Nichole.

Then he remembered the officers from the brothel. Could this mission have anything to do with their statements about Frank's being a *fine soldier*? Was he a threat to someone? Perhaps someone thought he knew something. Well, he didn't know from apple butter about those officers and their business. Was there a connection between Dame Metcalf and the on-base spy? Was one of the women who worked there involved with the spy? According to scuttlebutt, a woman might be involved. There had to be some reason for him to be sent on this mission with this green crew. But what was it?

"Frank, stop this crap and get this show on the road," he thought as he started going over the airplane with the pilot and co-pilot. He thought they should know how to do a simple visual preflight inspection. Wrong! They were jittery and it made him nervous thinking that these two men would soon be responsible for the lives of the crew—his life, especially.

He thought, "Guardian Angel, I hope you're watching all this and have a plan. I'm out on a limb and I know it. Help."

Finally, all was set and the green flare fired to signal *start the engines*. When all four engines were running, Frank thought, "Okay, at least they know how to do that." Then he remembered the crew had not walked the propellers through. The engines had started without creating a fire, so he guessed they were all right. The airplane began to roll from the hardstand, and then it stopped. Over the intercom, Frank heard the pilot say they had missed their spot in the taxi rotation.

After waiting for several minutes, they began to roll again. As Frank sat in the waist, he noticed a difference in the odor of this airplane. It smelled similar to that of a new car. This one had not yet picked up any odors from its human passengers. It had the odor of an airplane just like the one his crew had flown over from the States and left somewhere in Scotland.

Frank sat huddled in the radio room looking at the dark stains on his collar. His buddies were there with him: the mixed blood of Lieutenant Butt, Alex, and his friend who had walked into the propeller. He wore a proud badge of honor, as one might wear a medal for bravery. Perhaps he would join them this day, and maybe even on this same spot on this collar. He didn't care, just as long as it was quick. The memory of their voices filled his head. He also remembered Ashly's tender touch, his head in her lap—and then the hurt when he had discovered she was gone. He knew now that the cover over the tomb in his mind would never fully close.

The airplane started to roll down the runway and then with ease it lifted from the tarmac. The thirty-two 100-pound bombs were no problem for this airplane. The jet-black morning sky awaited them, and like knights in bright shining armor, the B-17 and its crew climbed for altitude, circling, spiraling ever upward.

Frank crawled into the ball turret and charged the two machine guns. Then he checked and rechecked everything. In the darkness of the morning before the rising of the sun, this crew flew toward a new life—a life about which they knew nothing. Frank was the oldest man on the crew, as even the pilot was two months his junior. He had seen the mystery of life and death before his eyes and he was ancient at twenty earth years!

The pilots were new at this game of forming into a 35-airplane formation in the dark morning sky, and when they missed their position in the formation, they were delegated to fly the *tail-end-Charlie* position, which, of course, was the least desirable position in a formation of bombers. Frank had been listening to the command radio and heard the pilot get his ass chewed out for missing his spot in formation. He was sure no one else on the crew knew how to use the radio other than the co-pilot. The rest of the crew would never know what had been said to the pilot.

The flight to Koln, Germany was not that exciting, other than when the crew saw their first flak coming up to greet them. They chattered excitedly over the intercom as if this were the greatest show on earth. The flak had been light and way off to one side, nowhere near their airplane. Frank said nothing as he sat, waiting for the real shit to hit the formation.

Ahead he saw the target, a railroad-marshaling yard filled with trains. Just as the bomb bay doors opened, all hell broke loose. Flak burst close to the airplane and they could hear it ripping the metal body of the new plane.

Then came a voice: "Clyde, this is the co-pilot. Get up here quick and help me get Lieutenant Moore off the stick . . . no, he's not injured . . . *The pilot has fainted*!"

"Holy shit!" thought Frank as the other bombers dropped bombs while his airplane circled and failed to drop a single bomb. And with that thought, the airplane went into a nosedive. Negative "g"-forces lifted Frank from his seat, slamming his head into the top of the turret. He was reaching for the door latches when all of a sudden he was pinned to his seat. He finally struggled from the turret, snapped on his parachute and made his way to the waist door. When he passed the waist gunners, they were standing around dumbfounded. He reached for the emergency release on the waist door, and as his hand grabbed for the release, he was pushed to the deck as the airplane suddenly leveled out. During the dive, they had descended from 25,000 down to 10,000 feet and the new airplane all but broke apart as it leveled out.

The bombardier yelled over the intercom, "What in hell was that for?"

The co-pilot told the bombardier, "I wanted to get him down where there was some air."

Frank thought, "Crap, the man was on oxygen! What good would fresh air do him?"

The airplane was lost from the formation and no one could see the other bombers. The navigator gave the co-pilot a heading and they flew for about half an hour, while the men up front tried to revive the first pilot. Since there was no flak and there were no German fighters, they just flew on. Frank sat in the waist with his parachute on, ready to jump.

After a half-hour of flying at 8,000 feet, Frank, who was looking out the window, keyed his mike and asked the navigator, "If we're flying west, sir, why is the sun shining in the right-side window?"

The navigator let out a loud, "*Aw, shit,*" over the intercom. "I gave a wrong heading. Turn the airplane around!"

The plane turned and headed back in the opposite direction, while the pilot was still out cold. Frank would later learn from the navigator that they had flown nearly to Austria before turning back.

No one was injured on the flight back to base and when the bomber stopped rolling, Frank jumped out, fell to his knees and kissed the tarmac. His Guardian Angel had pulled off another one. He looked up and there stood Don, Mark, Koop and King, who had been *sweating* him back to base on his final mission.

At the mess hall, the OIC gave Frank a double shot of Scotch, then added another, and Frank staggered to his seat. It was over! Done! He had completed 35 missions!

Frank's crewmates helped him to the hut and he sacked out with a tiredness he had never before felt. He was physically and emotionally exhausted. Drained of life. He drifted off to sleep and there they were as the cover slipped from the tomb in his mind, allowing the nightmares to return in a jumbled mess: flak bursts, screaming faces, a naked woman drifted by, dogs chased him, falling, a rock came crashing through a glass window, flashes of brilliant light, blinded, he felt his way along a slippery rock ledge.

"Wake up Frank, you're screaming! Wake up!" The voice of King brought him back to the real world. He remembered lying down to sleep. He also remembered he had accomplished something about which few ever lived to tell. He had completed the extra ten missions for General Doolittle—thirty-five combat missions with only a bruise on his heel. He was home free! It was over! Done! Finished 35 combat missions in just 135 days!

He sat up on the side of his bunk and questioned, "Why me? Why did I finish and Alex did not?"

He had nothing but memories in his head of his buddies. There was no relic of their ever having existed. Then he remembered his flight suit and the stains and headed to Supply to get a patch cut from the collar of his flight suit. He wanted a square inch where the bloodstains from his three buddies were mixed together. He would sew this patch on the inside of his blouse and would forever wear it with pride and honor.

"Sorry Frank, your suit went with some others to the cleaners in central supply. It had stains all over it. It's gone," said the supply sergeant.

Frank walked from the building until out of sight, and then he stopped and cried—and cried. They were gone! His friends, gone! God, how he had wanted that patch. They would remain in the tomb in his mind forever.

CHAPTER 26

Goodbye 385ᵗʰ Bomb Group

Frank did not go with the others to eat supper. He was not hungry and wanted to be alone with his thoughts. He walked out the back gate and down the road toward Stowmarket. After a while, he stopped and sat in the chilled night air, hoping it would help clear his mind. There was so much to consider, so many things he had to think out for himself. He remembered all the men who slept in the hut and were killed. How many? They numbered in the dozens. He remembered each by name, although he had tried not to know them. All would be awarded the Purple Heart, posthumously, and somewhere there would be a Gold Star placed in a window for each.

He thought of his Guardian Angel and how close he had been to his own death, except for a power greater than all mankind. He remembered making peace with his God and now he would have to honor that pact. God had done His part and now it was Frank's turn to make good.

What about Ashly and her child? There was something about that situation he had never been told. There had to be an underlying scheme for him to be involved. She had said something about continuing the clan bloodline. He had not listened all that well when she told him. Why had Dame Metcalf warned him that his life would be jeopardized if he made a move to see

Ashly or the child? He had to let all this go and continue with his life.

Frank expected to be called to HQ and offered a ground job at Great Ashfield, as most men in his position were given that choice. He could do that for any length of time. Then he thought of Nichole in London. Maybe he would be able to spend more time with her now and they could celebrate not having to worry about flying or him being killed.

After breakfast the next morning, Frank was called to squadron HQ and ordered to report to the flight surgeon at the base hospital for an examination. The doctor gave him a complete physical, the same old exam he had taken so many times before. It was passé. Skin it back and strip it down. Turn your head and cough. Now the other side. Bend over and spread 'em. The finger. Let me look in your ears. Open wide and say, "ahhhh." He did not know if the doctor had removed the rubber gloves or not, but he sure hoped he did. The doctor tapped his knees and elbows, then had him squat and stand. It was the works.

Then came the questions—fast, one after the other, until the doctor seemed to get serious with more questions. The gist was: "How stable are you, Frank Mays?" There were many things he would rather not answer, but he did so, as the doctor was very competent. He told of losing his best friends but did not mention the lost day after the funeral. Frank always wondered what he did during that time and who took care of him such that it cost him no money to travel. Of course, he would never know. Maybe that, too, had been his Guardian Angel.

Frank did not mention Ashly, but the doctor knew something as he asked about his Scottish girlfriend. Then he quickly let the question go before Frank could think of an answer. He wondered if everybody on base knew of his and Ashly's relationship. Why were they so interested?

The ability not to pay attention to nudity came in handy, as Frank was totally undressed before the doctor and a female nurse for over an hour. Hell, he was in no frame of mind to care who saw him. It had become a way of life for him here in England. He thought he would probably have to be careful of his actions and language if he ever got back to the States. People just would not understand how he had learned to live in this land of war.

The doctor wound up the exam by saying Frank needed lots of rest, something he could not get here on base. The doctor placed a sealed letter in his medical file that would go with him to a place where he could get the needed relaxation. It would be something like a rest home, maybe sort of like a hospital. The doctor did not give him any specifics about where he was going or when he would leave. It seemed as if the doctor was intentionally being evasive.

Frank was told to put his clothes on and wait in the front room for his file. He waited and waited until finally, a male nurse appeared with a sealed file and orders to report to squadron HQ.

It was after lunch when Frank met with the squadron CO. The meeting was brief—curt, like any true military meeting. "Sergeant Mays, you are hereby promoted to Technical Sergeant. Here are your orders. Pack your bags and be ready to travel in one hour. Report back here for your passage. Good luck, Sergeant Mays."

Frank saluted and left the office.

As he passed the First Sergeant, the man stopped him and without saying a word, he handed Frank an envelope, then turned his back to him. Frank walked from the room before stopping to look at what he had been handed. He wondered why everyone seemed to be less than kind toward him now. These people knew him well and now they acted as if he had a disease of some sort. Well, they could just kiss his ass. He was done flying and would be moved from the squadron. He did not owe them anything and neither did they owe him. He was even with this world.

He would miss his crewmates, having served together on all those bombing missions and shared the death of friends. But none were the same men he had known when they arrived here at the 385th. He thought he knew why; they were as screwed up as he was.

Outside the orderly room, Frank stopped and looked at the envelope. His name appeared on the outside, and in the same handwriting of the person who had asked him to come and talk about Ashly when she left. It was Dame Metcalf's handwriting! What in hell did she want this time? Maybe she had heard from Ashly and wanted him to know, he rationalized.

When he opened the envelope, his heart skipped a beat. It contained American money: 420 dollars—the exact amount he had loaned Swartz. No message, just money. He had kissed that money goodbye long ago, so why was she replacing the cash, and in American money? How did she know how much he had loaned Swartz?

Other than Alex, Frank had never told anyone about that money—not even Ashly. Nobody!

Swartz! Dame Metcalf must have had him by the balls and made him squeal. That was the only way it could have happened. What else was she into? Was he correct that she had been working with the military regarding the spy? Then he remembered something that had gone over his head when it was said. Captain Hudson, his marine lady friend, had said to him, "You are a fine soldier, but be careful."

That was what she had warned him about. The strange woman he had seen at the brothel had been Captain Hudson, and she was working on the leak of information at the base. She *had* been at the brothel and knew about him, but did not let him know. He wondered how much she knew about him and Ashly? How about that!

Frank wondered how Swartz fit into the whole matter. Maybe he was just as innocent as Frank was, just deep in debt and had a woman pregnant. Or the man could have been blackmailed by someone on base who knew of his activities. Who knows? He would let it go and thank his Guardian Angel.

Frank could not believe what was happening to him. Within twenty-four hours after the wheels on the airplane touched down upon completion of his 35th mission, he was out of the 385th Bomb Group and on a train headed to someplace in England named Stone. He felt he was given the *bums-rush* to get him away from Great Ashfield.

The CO had given him several items: a train ticket, his sealed file, a *Lucky Bastard* certificate and a handshake.

The men on his crew were as surprised as he was to

see him leave so fast. They still had another mission to fly to complete their tour of duty. He wondered if they would make it safely back home?

He would have liked to say goodbye to some of the men on base and maybe visit Dame Metcalf. Well, maybe that would not have been such a good idea. It seemed he had put himself in the wrong with everyone, and he was not sure just what he might have done. It had been the same as when he was home. He could never do anything to please his old man and always did something wrong no matter how hard he tried to please the man. It seemed he could not please anybody in the world.

Maybe it was just as well that he left quickly. To hell with everybody. He had pulled all 35 missions and few could say that. What more could they expect of him? He thought about what the doctor had said about his needing rest. The events of the past five or so months began to roll before his mind as he looked out the window at the peaceful English countryside.

His life had been one of life-versus-death. Love versus friendship. He still did not understand love. Who was prepared at a young age to remain loyal to one of the opposite sex? Look what happened to Alex when he found love. And Dana was also gone. Frank had thought he was learning love from Ashly, and then she had dropped him like a hot potato.

When he had first arrived here, Frank had been totally unaware of the effects of death on a person's state of mind. He had been forced to construct a tomb in his mind for all his dead friends. Then along came Ashly. Was his sense of friendship a showing of love? Could the act of sex bring one to accept a person as a life partner?

Was the bringing of a new life into the world by sex a bond strong enough to commit to a lifetime of love? He knew he could have loved Ashly, but she ran from him for a reason he could not understand. What was the difference between love and pure sexual satisfaction? Would it grow old to the point that one would seek new sex partners? With his friends, the sex thing was not a consideration. Could there be love without sex? It all remained a mystery to him.

Frank thought he had been a good soldier. He did not fear death; he respected it. There was no defeat other than death. Did death end love? What had ended his love with Ashly?

The railroad tracks were being repaired as the train made its way through the London yard, and Frank could see the craters where bombs had dropped the night before, ruining parts of the tracks. Paddington Station had been hit again and this time it looked like a bang-up job by the Germans. Frank's car was disconnected from the train and then reconnected without ever going into the station. People were shuffled about on the cars and then the train was underway again, heading for Stone.

He was unhappy that he did not get a chance to say goodbye to Nichole while in London. Would he ever see her again? It was doubtful. He was headed for *who knows where*.

A medic met Frank as he debarked the train in Stone. It was a short ride to a military hospital and during the jeep ride, the medic answered not even one of Frank's questions. Finally, Frank just stopped asking, as he thought the man was so evasive with his answers. He imagined he would find out something in a short while.

The hospital was like any temporary hospital, with wards connected by covered passageways. It was located on rolling hills near a small village named Stone in southern England. Frank was led to a ward that was broken into smaller rooms. After dropping his duffel and B-4 bags, he went to a mess hall where he found the food better than he had received at Great Ashfield. After eating, he went back to his room and made ready for some sack time.

He did not sleep well that night. The dreams—the nightmares—came when he did find sleep, and he finally lay awake most of the night, hoping to avoid the screaming faces and jumbled mess of his dreams.

The next morning, bright and early, they were getting him out of bed. It was only 6:00 a.m., but he was ready to get up and go find some coffee in the mess hall. Hot coffee, real GI coffee. It was like ambrosia to his nose. The food was nicely prepared and much better than the powdered stuff the base mess hall had served to the men of the 385th. He could only eat a little food, though, as he still became sick to his stomach in the mornings. He wished Ashly would hurry up and have her baby. Morning sickness must be giving her hell also.

The doctor examined Frank and gave him a clean bill of physical health, telling him that he didn't see many in as good condition as Frank. Frank showed him his souvenir, the piece of flak, and the doctor laughed and said that not many could have survived it. He said it must have been some bruise, as it was still slightly yellow. When the doctor got to the mental questions, Frank's tomb slid open and for two hours, the doctor drew the misery from him. He could not dodge the questions, but did manage to keep secret the day he had lost after the funeral.

The doctor was an older man, perhaps fifty, and he seemed to have compassion for Frank and his problems with losing so many friends. The doctor opened the sealed envelope from the base surgeon and read it, nodding his head as if in agreement with the other doctor's findings. Frank needed relief from stress and would be sent to a stateside hospital, something like a rest home, where he would receive treatment before consideration of further military service.

Frank thought the doctor had his head screwed on wrong. Hell, he was all right. He had finished all 35 combat missions and they did not have to tie him to a bed the way they had that pilot from his last mission. The last news on the pilot was that he was headed for the "loony-ward" somewhere. The others on that crew were screwed up also. That was why he had to replace the ball turret gunner on that mission. The man had freaked out at the last minute before the flight. Frank wished he had known about all that, as he might have been able to prepare for what happened on the mission. He had never heard of a pilot losing his nerve like that and really felt sorry for the man.

Frank could take anything the Army threw at him. Maybe it would be a rest home, such as the one he and the crew had enjoyed during their stand-down. He thought again of Alex. Damn, Alex was always there waiting for him to remember. All the people must have been just a thought away from the front of his mind.

The doctor continued with many questions and when finished, he wrote a letter and placed it with the one from the doctor at the 385th hospital. The doctor told Frank the letters would travel with him to his stateside destination and that he would arrange for Frank to travel on a hospital ship back to the States.

Frank was at Stone only for about ten days before receiving word that he was shipping out. With his bags inspected and sealed, he was sent by train to a seaport in southern England called Southampton.

CHAPTER 27

Goodbye England

Frank mailed a letter to Nichole, although he had no idea if it would ever be delivered. He wrote the address from memory and was not sure if he had it correct. If it were delivered, maybe she would write to his hometown address in the States; otherwise, she would probably think he had gone to be with her Alfred.

He smiled when he wrote the letter and remembered all the good times they had together. He wondered why his leaving Nichole did not affect him the same as had Ashly's leaving him. He reasoned it was because she was always fun and had no hang-ups, except for her Alfred. He knew she had really loved that guy. There was no way he could have replaced Alfred anymore than she could replace Ashly.

Frank boarded a ship named *Salturnia*, and was placed in a ward with ten other men. He was given pajamas but allowed to keep and wear his class-A uniform. The ship left port on November 2, 1944, under the cover of darkness.

The Army doctor on board the ship went over Frank's files and opened the sealed letters. He seemed to find everything the same as the other doctors and gave Frank more pills to take to help him sleep. The doctor wrote additional information and resealed his letter with the other two.

Frank was given free run, but only on the deck on which his ward was located. There were male officers on the deck above and females on the deck above that. Frank heard there was a nymphomaniac loose up there and they were not sure what might happen unless she was found. She had been missing from the moment she boarded the ship.

For two days, it was an enjoyable voyage, as the seas were calm. Frank sneaked up on the main deck forward and saw about thirty ships in the convoy, with destroyers cruising the perimeter. A steady 15-knot breeze was blowing as they headed south toward the Azores.

Most of the men in Frank's ward were bedridden and he helped by talking and listening. He retrieved items for the men and helped the medics feed them. He walked the long corridors where the badly injured were kept in small cabins, and was not at a loss for words when someone wanted to talk. The soldiers, some his age but most a little older, responded to his kindness and for a while, they forgot their pain and laughed with him as he told funny tales of his adventures. Some of his stories about ghosts interested the men. They asked him to return and talk every day and he was happy to see smiles on their faces when he entered a room. Who the hell needed a hospital? Not Frank! He was up and about, constantly helping others.

Maybe it was his southern drawl, or his ever-present smile, or it could have been the Lifebuoy soap that he used. Or it could have been the understanding of one who has *been there-done that*, one who came through it all. Or just maybe it was nothing more than friends were everywhere and one just had to look for them. Whatever the reason, the soldiers seemed comfortable talking with Frank.

Then the storm hit. It could have been a hurricane. Swells reached fifty feet in height and the ship yawed, pitched and rolled constantly, seeming as if it might founder at any moment. Most of the patients and many of the medics were sick to near the point of death—but not Frank. He became as one of the staff, a medic, tending both patients and staff, as they needed his help with upchucks, bedpans, and baths.

The sea continued to beat against the hull of the ship, sounding as if it might tear it apart. For three days and two nights, the storm raged, while most people on the ship remained deathly seasick. The only food served was cheese and saltine crackers, but even that did not stay down. Frank removed his blouse, rolled up his sleeves and became a deckhand in the ward and other places as needed. He was a mop-and-bucket scrub boy and a medic, other than dressing wounds, which he left to the doctors and one nurse who was surviving without being seasick.

Frank held the hand of one soldier in a full body cast to help calm his fear. This fear that Frank saw on the ship was something he had never before experienced. Many were near death from fright, as they could not help themselves. Ashly had taught Frank some things, and among them was how to bathe and dry a male. It was not a job he liked, but he did manage to clean bottoms after an accident.

When the storm ended and things began to return to normal, the doctors and medics thanked Frank repeatedly, telling him that he had been the difference in taking care of the soldiers. He had worked hard and given no quarters for his new friends. The men showed their thanks in different ways and always wanted him near them. They smiled when he entered a room and he made many new friends, some of which would not live to debark the ship.

The odor of infected flesh hung thick in the air. It really bothered Frank when he went into a room and the soldier had been removed to the morgue. His tomb started to overflow with all his new lost friends.

In his ward, one patient wanted to teach him to tie sailor knots and another wanted him to play cards. One wanted a drink of water. The water came first, then on to the others. He was being put to some sort of test but it would not break his spirit. After all, he had a Guardian Angel!

Frank thought of the many people with whom he had come in contact while overseas. How had he influenced their lives? How had they influenced his? He was thankful for all his experiences, as it had forced him to grow into a man. His memory took him back to that young teenager who landed in Scotland late one evening. He had been full of himself back then. Now he sat here feeling as ancient as the ocean upon which he sailed. Six months—a lifetime, maybe several lifetimes—with his friends, both male and female. The good times outweighed the bad, but the bad was not easily forgotten and brought tears to his eyes. How he hurt inside. He knew he must try to forget. They must remain in his tomb, far from his memory.

But not you Alex, I need you to help me keep my sanity. Alex, my only true friend.

Frank heard that the nymph was found hiding on the

officers' deck, where she had been smuggled by one of the officers, who kept her there for four days. It was the talk of the ship. Well, maybe someone had enjoyed the storm. Frank returned and told the tale to the men in his ward and it brought lots of laughter. They made jokes about him not being a part of that action as he might have been able to get her in the ward for them.

It made Frank feel good for the men to say things that indicated they missed him when he was absent. Damn good! They asked what it was like topside, about the weather, and about what the rest of the ship looked like. Would he write something for them in a diary or a letter? What were his ribbons for? *How about lighting my cigarette for me and hold it for a puff or two.*

He listened to many tales told in low voices, tales of a soldier's horror. Some were told with tears and he wiped them from their faces. He remembered Alex wiping his face with that damned oily rag. There had been tears in Alex's eyes, too, as he looked at Frank. That had to be some sort of love. Was love the same as was happening here? Would he ever learn to love?

It had been eleven days since the ship left England. In a conversation with a doctor, Frank found out the ship was three days out from New York. They were scheduled to dock on the New Jersey side of the harbor, as it would be easier to move the men to hospitals from there rather than through the busy New York port. The Army had made all arrangements to transfer him and the other soldiers to hospitals.

The pills given him were having the desired effect and he felt much better than when he had boarded the ship. His stomach even took the food now without him losing it.

One evening Frank decided to go topside and watch the sunset. As he neared the bow of the ship on the main deck, he heard a voice, but the speaker was out of sight. The voice was describing the sunset, so he stopped and listened as he watched the bottom rim of the sun touch the ocean.

"The waxen surface is reflecting golden sunlight as wavelets move through the water. Mixed with the gold are brilliant flashes of silver racing toward the horizon where they burst into the orange ball of the half-set sun. The water close to the ship is gray-azure, blending to ebony at the distant horizon. A wisp of baby-pink clouds is scattered against a blue sky, and the ocean haze over the water seems afire. As the top rim of the sun disappears, the sky blooms orange-red and clouds start to darken to a deep gray as the world comes to the cusp of another night."

Frank remained transfixed as he watched and listened to the voice describing exactly the sight he was seeing. Then Frank saw the man who had been speaking. With him was another man, both of them in full-dress marine uniforms. One was on crutches and the other had patches over his eyes. The marine on crutches led his buddy from the bow, back past Frank to the bulkhead hatch. Frank stepped up, opened the hatch and held it for them as they smiled and stepped through.

Frank leaned against the bulkhead with his chest rising and falling as his mind flooded with thoughts of what he had just seen and heard. The two marine buddies reminded him so much of Alex and himself. The tender caring between the men reminded Frank of the day before when a soldier had told of how he received his wounds. The Air Force had bombed his unit at St. Lo and he was injured. He was recovered and sent to a hospital in England where he stayed until boarding this ship. Many men had been killed in the bombing. Frank then told the soldier of his part in the bombing and how it had disturbed him. As tears filled Frank's eyes, the soldier laid a hand on his arm as if to say "It's okay, buddy. I understood."

What about all the other people that he had a part in killing? The cities that he saw as firestorms. How many people? There had to be defenseless women and children among the dead on those air raids. Entire families. The German soldiers? How many? The pilots in the ME-109s he had shot down? They also had caring buddies.

He questioned why he was on this hospital ship now. That score of 160 on the IQ test didn't mean a damned thing. They were wrong. He had learned to kill and was good at doing just that. One doesn't need smarts to kill soldiers—soldiers with buddies—soldiers with thoughts the same as his own. Did they also have to build a tomb in their mind for their buddies, the same as he? Yes! They were no different from him. Everybody lost. There was nothing to gain. He wondered what it had been like for the British people having suffered four or more years of bombings and the loss of so many of their young men. There had also been many women and children lost in England.

The cool salty night air cut across Frank's face as he realized that the reality of life did bring forth love. The men on this ship had proven that. What was this love? There had to be more than one kind of love. Sex was not love! Whatever love was, Frank was glad he knew it.

He walked to the bow of the ship and looked ahead. Out there in the distance was the United States of America.

Home. He was going home.

Behind him lay all the things of war and memories of people he had met—and his Princess. He would forever remember them all. He still had more questions than answers, though. Why? *Why* about so many things? He was taking these questions home with him.

Frank had kept a log of his missions, which added up to more than 250 hours in the air over Germany. He still had a light yellow spot on his left heel, which he thought of as his personalized badge of honor. It had even been immortalized in art. He again fingered the piece of shrapnel in his pocket.

On his chest, he proudly wore his combat badges:

> The Distinguished Flying Cross
> The Air Medal with four Oak Leaf Clusters
> The European Battle Ribbon with a Silver Star
> The Good Conduct Medal
> A Presidential Citation
> His Silver Wings over a blue Combat Patch . . .

AND NO PURPLE HEART!

Note: The Eighth Air Force awarded more than 65,000 Purple Heart Medals for Airmen killed or wounded during the bombing raids over France and Germany from August 1943 to April 1945. Most were awarded between February and October 1944.

EPILOGUE

When Technical Sergeant Frank Mays debarked the hospital ship in New Jersey, his medical records from Great Ashfield and Stone England, along with those from the shipboard doctor, were all *lost*! *Gone*! *Nowhere to be found*! *File Thirteen*!

After some confusion, he was sent on furlough with orders to report to Byrd Field in Richmond, Virginia. The missing medical files and letters still could not be located, so in true military fashion, new records were *manufactured* where needed, and he was not reexamined.

Upon completion of further training, Frank was placed on a new combat crew and later found himself on a B-29 Super Flying Fortress destined for the Pacific war zone.

After the two *Atomic Bombs* were dropped on Japan in August 1945, Frank was up for discharge from the Air Corps.

On September 19, 1945, Sergeant Frank Mays became a civilian.

He spent the next 54 years in and out of civilian and Veteran Administration hospitals, suffering from a condition now known as "Post Traumatic Syndrome."

"Never . . . Never give up!"

—Winston Churchill

Frank Reese Mays
in ball turret

The War Horse and her crew